# 3D

# CONSTRUCTION

# MODELING

*SketchUp* 4.0
INCLUDED

# PROJECT BASED LEARNING

## DENNIS FUKAI

5th Printing: January 2006
by Alta Systems Inc, Gainesville FL 32653

a publication of

I n s i t e b u i l d e r s . c o m
16708 SW 132nd Lane
Archer FL 32618
(352) 870-9357

babs@insitebuilders.com

# ACKNOWLEDGEMENTS

Special thanks to Mark Carvalho of @Last Sofware, Inc. for his unfailing support of architectural and construction education.

Also thanks to Sara Strebe and Jim Holman of @Last software and Mike Lucey, Phillip Meadows, David Mihm, John Yurko, Archutek and the other experts who lend their time and talent to the SketchUp Users Forum < http://sketchup.com/forum.

Not to forget Barbara Fukai, the editor, coordinator, marketer and publisher who made this book physically possible.

And finally, thanks to the hundreds of students who stumbled, bumbled and burned the midnight oil to come up with this simple and better way to model the construction process.

## CONSERVE YOUR MINUTES
You have 8 free hours, 480 long minutes. Be sure to close the SketchUp program when not in use or when you take a "quick" break.

CLICK SAVE

## SAVE AND SAVE OFTEN
SketchUp automatically saves a back up file, but you never know. In fact, to be extra safe, regularly save new files under different names on a separate disk or in different folders on your hard-drive.

## SHORTIES
The **"shorties"** are quick and simple movies that demonstrate the model construction techniques. Look for the **shorties** icon as you work through the book. The videos are on the companion CD and can be paused and played again and again.

*Dennis Fukai is a licensed architect and construction manager with more than thirty years experience as a professional construction administrator, researcher, and university professor. He is a Fulbright Scholar and earned his PhD in architecture from the University of California, Berkeley. Dennis has been recognized internationally for his work in advanced construction modeling and graphic communications.*

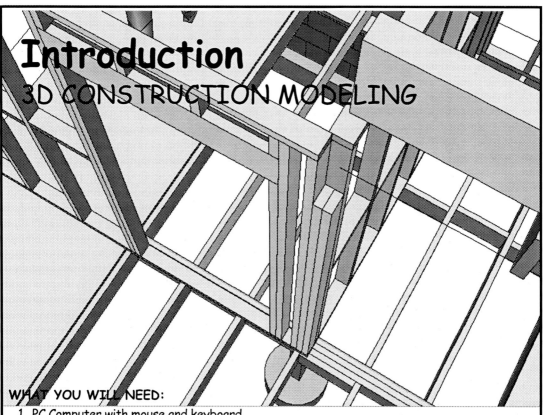

# Introduction
## 3D CONSTRUCTION MODELING

**WHAT YOU WILL NEED:**

1. PC Computer with mouse and keyboard
2. Windows operating system*
3. Access to the WWW (not essential)
4. A CD drive to access the book's CD
6. A folder named SketchUp
   on your computer's desktop

SketchUpFiles

**WHAT YOU WILL DO:**

1. Visit and review the SketchUp Website
2. Download the Trial program
3. Install the program *SketchUp⁴·⁰*

4. View the "What is SketchUp" videos
5. View the Start Here videos
6. View the Key Concepts video
7. View <u>some</u> Selected Videos

8. Look at the SketchUp interface
9. Look at the 10 steps of the book

**SOME WORDS TO KNOW:**

<u>CLICK</u>: press and release left mouse button

<u>Components</u>: independent piece of the model

<u>Construction Model</u>: built from pieces

<u>DOUBLE CLICK</u>: two quick CLICKs

<u>Download</u>: transfer a file to your computer

<u>DRAG</u>: press and hold mouse button

<u>Installer</u>: a file that loads a program

<u>LEFT CLICK</u>: CLICK the left mouse button

<u>Objects</u>: 3D lines and surfaces

<u>Page</u>: a saved view of a model

<u>Pallete</u>: a common collection of tools

<u>RIGHT CLICK</u>: CLICK right mouse button

<u>Tools</u>: Toolbar and Menu utilities

*The MAC version looks different but is very similar
and follows the same model construction process

## Download the Latest Trial Program

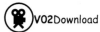
On the **Web** go to **WWW.SketchUp.com** and take a look at the **SketchUp** website*

CLICK "Test Drive" to **download** the latest version of the **SketchUp** program

**Fill out** the form and **CLICK** to Download

*Some videos are on the companion CD

---

The **download process** is a matter of clicking links to place the **installer** on your **computer**

CLICK to confirm the download

**Save** to a **new** SketchUp folder

---

When the **download is complete**, go to the SketchUp folder and **Open** the installer

DOUBLE CLICK the installer to **install** the program on **your computer**

SketchUp **installs** this **shortcut** on the desktop

---

While **still online** DOUBLE CLICK the shortcut on your desktop....

Then CLICK the **Tutorials** link to view the videos on the **SketchUp** website

**DON'T OPEN THE PROGRAM YET!!**
Save your 8 hours (480 MINUTES***) as long as you can by first reviewing a few quick SketchUp videos

***That's a lot of time if you remember to close the program when not in use -- even for a minute

2

# First the Tutorials*

To access the Tutorials index **CLICK** the **Training** link and then CLICK **Tutorials***

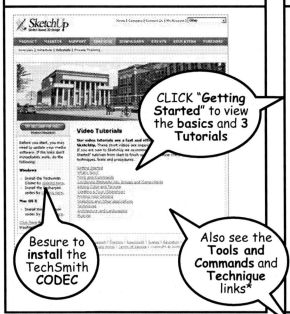

> CLICK "**Getting Started**" to view the **basics** and 3 **Tutorials**

> Besure to **install** the TechSmith **CODEC**

> Also see the **Tools and Commands** and **Technique** links*

*These are the ones important to construction modeling

---

**Getting Started** covers the **basics** of the tools, 3D environment, and modeling.

### Using the Mouse
Clarifies LEFT, RIGHT CLICK, DOUBLE CLICK, DRAG, etc**

### Getting Started
The fundamentals of the SketchUp interface and tools

### Drawing With Inferences
An overview of the modeling potential of SketchUp

### Common Mistakes
Common errors and how to get out of trouble, a must see

Takes about 38 total minutes**

---

The **3 Tutorials** cover **concepts** like edges, surfaces, comera tools, and **inferences**

### Tutorial 1
Drawing Lines and using the Push/Pull tool

### Tutorial 2
Drawing Rectangles, Panning, Zooming, and Inferences

### Tutorial 3
Drawing with Inferences, Construction lines, Protractor

Takes about 9 total minutes**

---

"**Tools and Commands**" and "**Techniques**" cover **construction modeling** methods

### Rotating
Rotating and copying surfaces and objects

### Inference Locking
Snapping and aligning objects together as an assembly

### Grouping
Keeping objects separated so that they can be assembled

### Using Layers
Assembly comments and notes to highlight important areas

Takes about 10 total minutes***

---

**If videos skip or do not play, download and Save them to your computer before viewing

***OK, OK, view the rest later if you can't take any more. But do view them all as soon as you can

# The SketchUp Interface

Now look at the **SketchUp** interface below.  There's **no need to memorize** Menus, Tools, or Commands, you'll pick them up **as you build** your model.  Just get a feel for the Interface before you open the program.  Also read the **Quick Reference guide** on the next page.

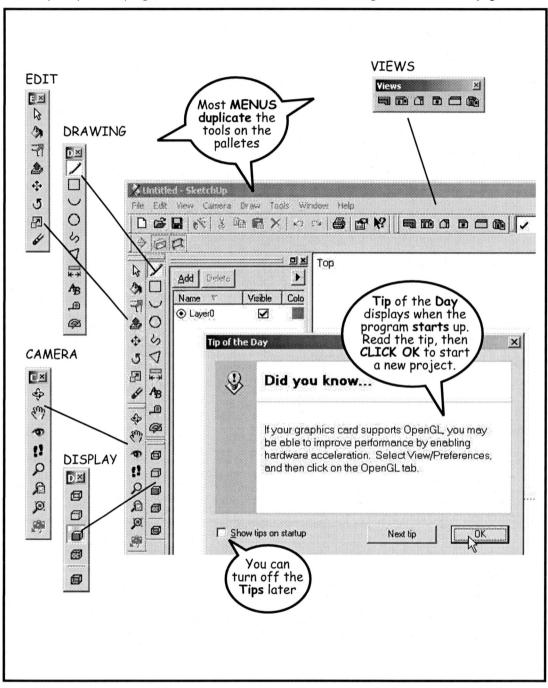

VIEWS

EDIT

Most **MENUS** duplicate the tools on the palletes

DRAWING

CAMERA

DISPLAY

**Tip** of the **Day** displays when the program **starts** up. Read the tip, then **CLICK OK** to start a new project.

Did you know...

If your graphics card supports OpenGL, you may be able to improve performance by enabling hardware acceleration.  Select View/Preferences, and then click on the OpenGL tab.

☐ Show tips on startup    Next tip    OK

You can turn off the **Tips** later

4

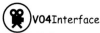
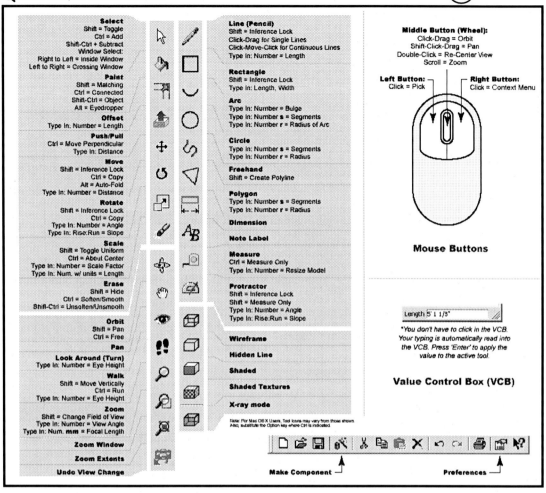

**Select**
Shift = Toggle
Ctrl = Add
Shift-Ctrl + Subtract
Window Select:
Right to Left = Inside Window
Left to Right = Crossing Window

**Paint**
Shift = Matching
Ctrl = Connected
Shift-Ctrl = Object
Alt = Eyedropper

**Offset**
Type In: Number = Length

**Push/Pull**
Ctrl = Move Perpendicular
Type In: Distance

**Move**
Shift = Inference Lock
Ctrl = Copy
Alt = Auto-Fold
Type In: Number = Distance

**Rotate**
Shift = Inference Lock
Ctrl = Copy
Type In: Number = Angle
Type In: Rise:Run = Slope

**Scale**
Shift = Toggle Uniform
Ctrl = About Center
Type In: Number = Scale Factor
Type In: Num. w/ units = Length

**Erase**
Shift = Hide
Ctrl = Soften/Smooth
Shift-Ctrl = Unsoften/Unsmooth

**Orbit**
Shift = Pan
Ctrl = Free

**Pan**

**Look Around (Turn)**
Type In: Number = Eye Height

**Walk**
Shift = Move Vertically
Ctrl = Run
Type In: Number = Eye Height

**Zoom**
Shift = Change Field of View
Type In: Number = View Angle
Type In: Num. mm = Focal Length

**Zoom Window**

**Zoom Extents**

**Undo View Change**

**Line (Pencil)**
Shift = Inference Lock
Click-Drag for Single Lines
Click-Move-Click for Continuous Lines
Type In: Number = Length

**Rectangle**
Shift = Inference Lock
Type In: Length, Width

**Arc**
Type In: Number = Bulge
Type In: Number s = Segments
Type In: Number r = Radius of Arc

**Circle**
Type In: Number s = Segments
Type In: Number r = Radius

**Freehand**
Shift = Create Polyline

**Polygon**
Type In: Number s = Segments
Type In: Number r = Radius

**Dimension**

**Note Label**

**Measure**
Ctrl = Measure Only
Type In: Number = Resize Model

**Protractor**
Shift = Inference Lock
Shift = Measure Only
Type In: Number = Angle
Type In: Rise:Run = Slope

**Wireframe**

**Hidden Line**

**Shaded**

**Shaded Textures**

**X-ray mode**

Note: For Mac OS X Users, Tool icons may vary from those shown.
Also, substitute the Option key where Ctrl is indicated.

**Middle Button (Wheel):**
Click-Drag = Orbit
Shift-Click-Drag = Pan
Double-Click = Re-Center View
Scroll = Zoom

**Left Button:**
Click = Pick

**Right Button:**
Click = Context Menu

**Mouse Buttons**

Length 5' 1 1/3"

*You don't have to click in the VCB.
Your typing is automatically read into
the VCB. Press 'Enter' to apply the
value to the active tool.

**Value Control Box (VCB)**

Make Component ⌐
Preferences ⌐

5

## DO YOU KNOW HOW TO:

1. Get around and use the SketchUp Website
2. Use the Try & Buy page and download the program
3. Install the SketchUp program on your computer
4. "What is SketchUp" as shown on the first video
5. The basic commands shown on the Start Here videos
6. Do most of the things shown on the Key Concepts video
7. Do most of the things shown on the Selected Videos
8. The general layout of the SketchUp interface

READY

OK, take a look
at the
**10 STEPS**

The _Construction Model_ you're going to build will give you **hands on** experience. We'll take it step by step. **10 steps to be precise.** Be sure to **take a minute** to view the **shorties** as you go along, it's a lot easier **after you see** it done.

**STEP 01:** Setup the model, insert a plat map, build a 3D model base
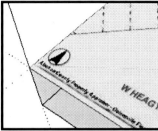

**STEP 02:** Scale and orient the site to the real world
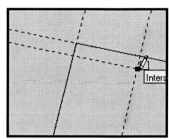

**STEP 03:** layout the site conditions and setbacks and start a Work Plan

**STEP 04:** Excavate the site from the workpoint by cutting into the model base
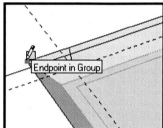

**STEP 05:** Form and pour footings and build a concrete block stem wall
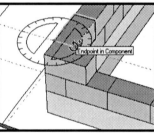

**STEP 06:** Set sills and floor joists and sheathing to frame the floor
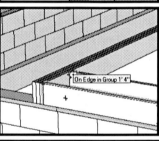

**STEP 07:** Frame stud walls in a layout area and tilt and move into place
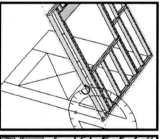

**STEP 08:** Frame the roof with rafters, shear and bearing walls

**STEP 09:** Try the various SketchUp animation and display tools

**STEP 10:** Test your proficiency and review the process
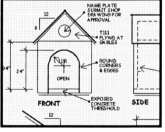

# Step01: Model SetUp
## 3D CONSTRUCTION MODELING

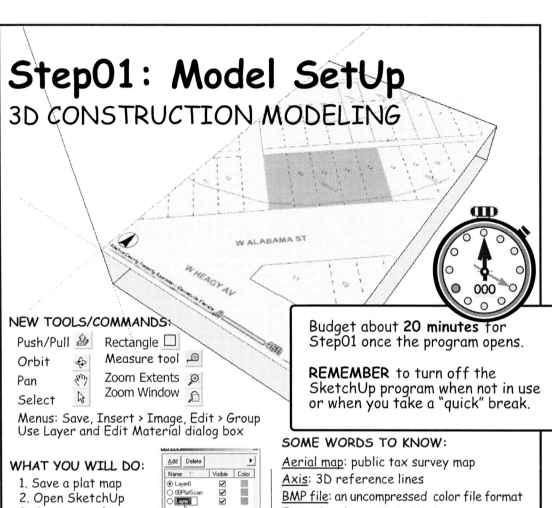

### NEW TOOLS/COMMANDS:

| | | | |
|---|---|---|---|
| Push/Pull | 🖎 | Rectangle | ☐ |
| Orbit | ✥ | Measure tool | 🖭 |
| Pan | ✋ | Zoom Extents | 🔎 |
| Select | ▷ | Zoom Window | 🔍 |

Menus: Save, Insert > Image, Edit > Group
Use Layer and Edit Material dialog box

### WHAT YOU WILL DO:

1. Save a plat map
2. Open SketchUp
3. Create new layers

4. Insert the plat map into SketchUp
5. View the plat map in 3D
6. Try the other tools on the View toolbar
7. Size the plat map to the real world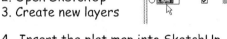
8. Orbit the plat map to view underside
9. Draw a rectangle under the plat map
10. Extrude the rectangle into 3D
11. Turn off the plat map layer
12. Change layer color and transparency
13. Group the box as a separate model object

Budget about **20 minutes** for Step01 once the program opens.

**REMEMBER** to turn off the SketchUp program when not in use or when you take a "quick" break.

### SOME WORDS TO KNOW:

<u>Aerial map</u>: public tax survey map
<u>Axis</u>: 3D reference lines
<u>BMP file</u>: an uncompressed color file format
<u>Extrude</u>: elongating a 2D shape
<u>Group</u>: a collection of lines and surfaces
<u>Inference</u>: SketchUp position reference
<u>JPEG</u>: a compression format for a BMP file
<u>KEY IN</u>: direct input from the keyboard
<u>Layer</u>: separates objects in model space
<u>Model Base</u>: the box the model is built on
<u>Object</u>: a Group or component in the model
<u>Origin</u>: the intersection of all 3 axes
<u>Plat map</u>: a map that shows property lines
<u>RGB</u>: red, green, blue color mix
<u>Scale bar</u>: graphic dimension indicator
<u>Scan</u>: a BMP file created by a copy scanner
<u>TIFF</u>: a high resolution BMP file

## Start with the Site...

Put the **book's CD** into your computer's **CD Drive** and look for the aerial and **plat** maps...

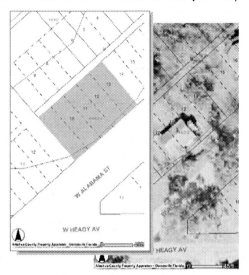

**Plat maps** and **aerials** like these can be found on most county and city tax **collector websites**. You can also **scan** a survey or plot plan from the **construction drawings**

Almost **any image** can be inserted and scaled if there's a **dimensional reference** (like a street, property line, or scale bar).

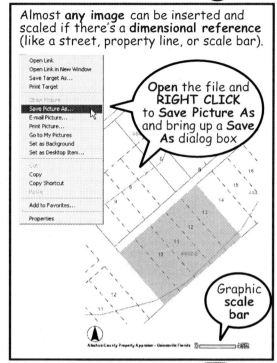

**Open** the file and **RIGHT CLICK** to **Save Picture As** and bring up a **Save As** dialog box

Graphic **scale bar**

When the dialog box comes up, name the file and **Save** it onto **your computer**...

CLICK on the **Save as type** option to set the file type to JPEG* before you CLICK Save

FINALLY we open the program. Remember **every minute counts** so watch your clock. **Figure 20 minutes for Step01.**

DOUBLE CLICK the shortcut on your Desktop and then CLICK Continue

*JPEG files use less memory in SketchUp

# Insert the Plat Map

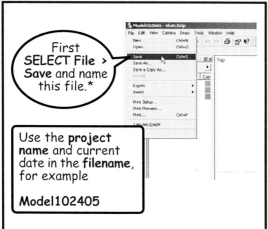

First **SELECT File > Save** and name this file.*

Use the **project name** and current date in the **filename**, for example

**Model102405**

*SketchUp regularly saves a backup.

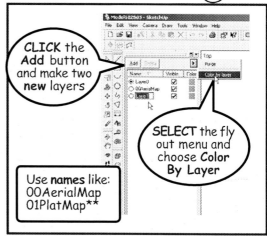

**CLICK** the **Add** button and make two **new** layers

**SELECT** the fly out menu and choose **Color By Layer**

Use **names** like:
00AerialMap
01PlatMap**

**Using numbers in the names keeps the layers in order

---

The plat **map file** will be part of the base of the construction **model**

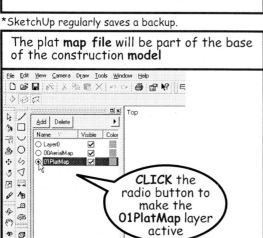

**CLICK** the radio button to make the **01PlatMap** layer active

Note that you can also **Insert Components** and **DWG** or **AutoCAD** files (and Export...)

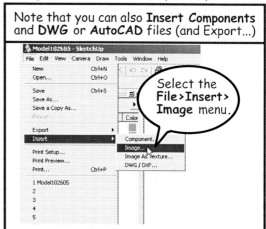

Select the **File>Insert> Image** menu.

---

When the **Insert Image** box comes up, browse to the **JPEG** you saved to **insert**

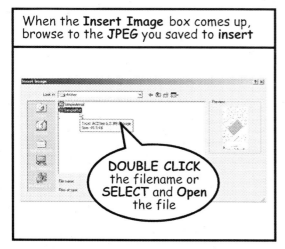

**DOUBLE CLICK** the filename or **SELECT** and **Open** the file

As soon as you click in the Insert Image dialog box, the image is immediately **attached** to your **cursor**.

When you move the mouse, the plat **map moves** with it.

**But don't CLICK yet!**

Cursor

VO8Plat

DOUBLE-CLICK to drop the **JPEG** into model space on the **active OOPlatScan layer.** The plat map is a visual reference that **orients the model** to the actual site conditions.

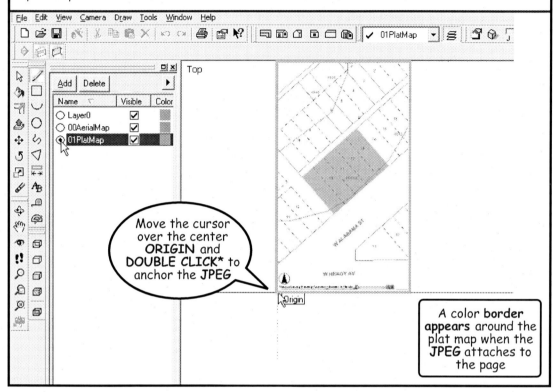

Move the cursor over the center **ORIGIN** and **DOUBLE CLICK*** to anchor the **JPEG**

A color **border appears** around the plat map when the **JPEG** attaches to the page

*If you **CLICK** once instead of a **DOUBLE CLICK**, the image will drop anchor on the page and shrink and expand as you move the cursor. If that happens **PRESS** the **Escape Key** or go to **UNDO** in the Edit Menu and try the **Insert** again.

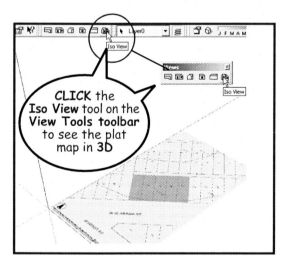

CLICK the **Iso View** tool on the **View Tools toolbar** to see the plat map in **3D**

Remember the other tools on the **Views Toolbar** display other **preset** views of the model...**

**You can also turn off Perspective in the View Menu to flatten the elevations to 2D

# View the 2D Map in 3D

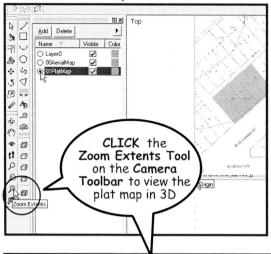

The tools on the **Camera Toolbar** change point of view and the model's position...

- Orbit
- Pan
- Look around
- Walk
- Zoom
- Zoom Window
- Zoom Extents
- Undo View Change

CLICK the **Zoom Extents Tool** on the **Camera Toolbar** to view the plat map in 3D

---

The tools on the **View** and **Camera** toolbars change the **2D JPEG** into a **3D object**. You can also use them to change your view point or the placement of **the model**...

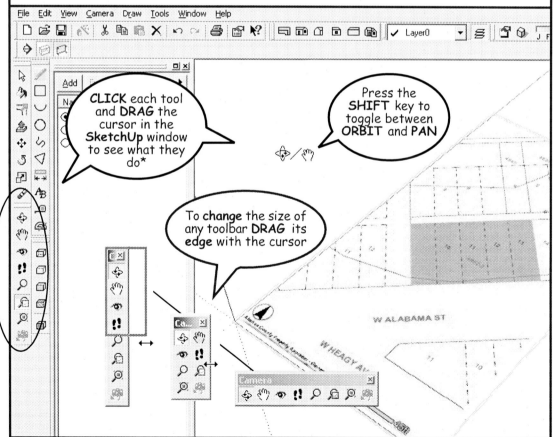

CLICK each tool and **DRAG** the cursor in the **SketchUp** window to see what they do*

Press the **SHIFT** key to toggle between **ORBIT** and **PAN**

To **change** the size of any toolbar **DRAG** its **edge** with the cursor

*To conserve your minutes, be sure to close the program when not in use or you take a break...

# Scale the JPEG to the Real World

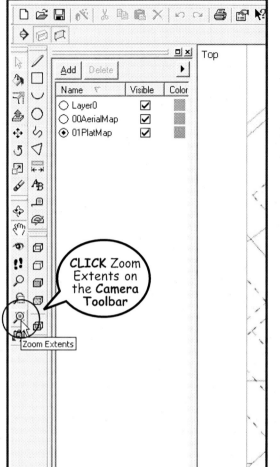

CLICK Zoom Extents on the **Camera Toolbar**

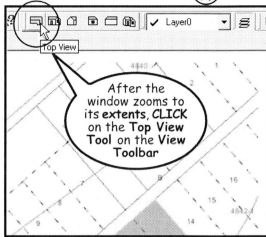

After the window zooms to its **extents, CLICK** on the **Top View Tool** on the **View Toolbar**

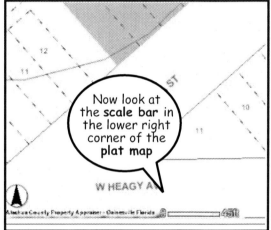

Now look at the **scale bar** in the lower right corner of the **plat map**

CLICK the **Measure Tool**...

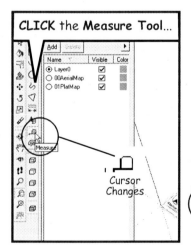

Cursor Changes

CLICK Zoom Window tool...

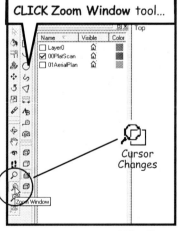

Cursor Changes

DRAG a **Zoom Window**...*

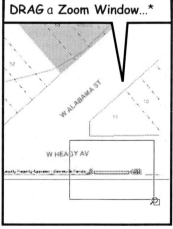

*The **Measure** tool returns immediately after the zoom window command has been completed

# Scale the Scan to the Real World

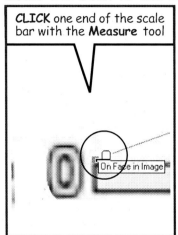

CLICK one end of the scale bar with the **Measure** tool

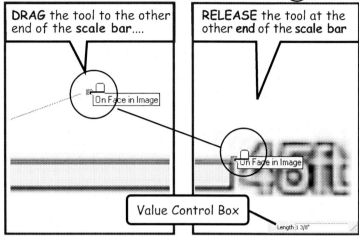

DRAG the tool to the other end of the **scale bar**....

RELEASE the tool at the other **end** of the **scale bar**

On Face in Image

On Face in Image

On Face in Image

Value Control Box

Length 1 3/8"

---

Immediately **KEY IN 45'** and press **ENTER***

No need to **CLICK** in the Value Control Box before typing.

Also note the 0 and the < " > mark are **not necessary when entering just feet**

But don't forget the apostrophe mark < ' > after the 45 feet

The **Value Control Box** shows the **approximate*** length of the JPEG...

## 1' - 3 3/8"

Length 1 3/8"

The **length** of the scale bar in the **real world** is...

## 45' - 0"

Length 45'

*The keyboard is a SketchUp model by Phillip Meadows

---

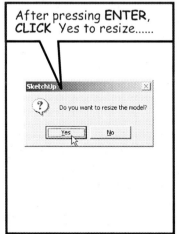

After pressing **ENTER**, **CLICK** Yes to resize......

SketchUp

? Do you want to resize the model?

Yes    No

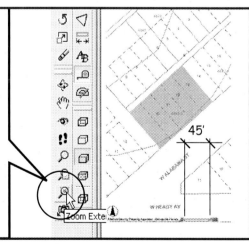

The plat map will seem to **disappear**, but...

**CLICK  Zoom Extents** again to view the **resized** image.

The scan may **look** the **same**, but its dimension is about **45' 0".***
(The same as the **real world**).

Zoom Exte...

45'

*In SketchUp, everything is "approximate"

CLICK SAVE

The **SAVE** icon is at the top left of the window. **Control S also saves.**

You can insert an aerial photo, or any other image, and scale it in the same way. **Here's what you do** (did!!):

1. **Create a JPEG\* image file** (or other bitmap):
   - Scan a map, plat, or aerial photo, or...
   - RIGHT CLICK & Save the file to your computer

2. **Open the SketchUp file**
   - Create a Layer for the JPEG, make it active
   - Use File > Insert Menu to insert the JPEG
   - DOUBLE CLICK the JPEG image into SketchUp
   - Use a known dimension to resize the JPEG
   - Welcome to the real world of 3D modeling

\*JPEG image files are smaller and require less memory

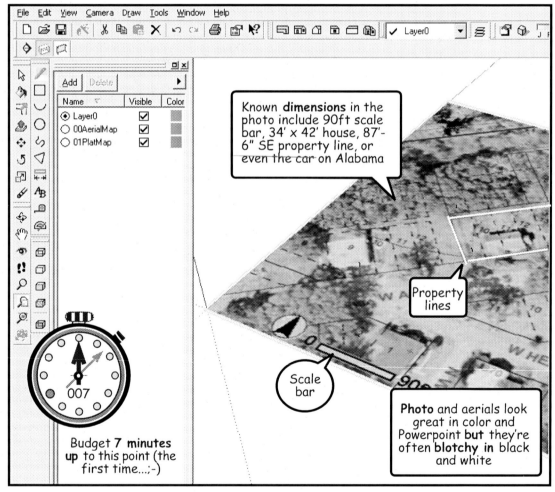

Known **dimensions** in the photo include 90ft scale bar, 34' x 42' house, 87'-6" SE property line, or even the car on Alabama

Property lines

Scale bar

Budget **7 minutes up** to this point (the first time...;-)

**Photo** and aerials look great in color and Powerpoint **but** they're often **blotchy in** black and white

14

## View the Underside of the JPEG

Before you start, **SELECT** Windows > **Display Settings** to view **different settings.**

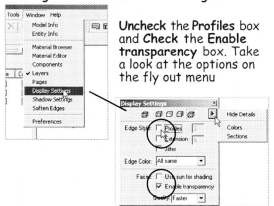

**Uncheck** the **Profiles** box and **Check** the **Enable transparency** box. Take a look at the options on the fly out menu

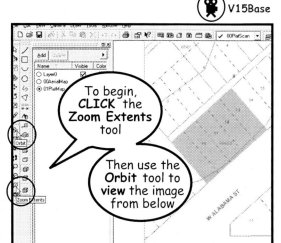

To begin, **CLICK** the **Zoom Extents** tool

Then use the **Orbit** tool to **view** the image from below

---

**DRAG** the **Orbit** tool...

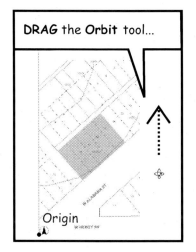

Origin

---

**DRAG** the tool upward...

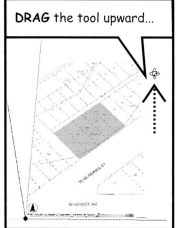

---

**CLICK** and **DRAG**...

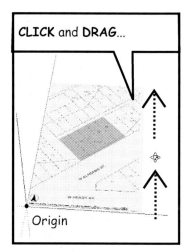

Origin

---

**CLICK** and **DRAG** again...

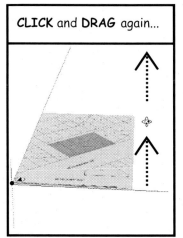

---

**DRAG** until you see the...

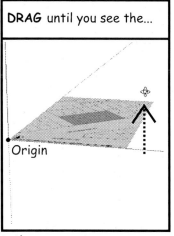

Origin

---

**Underside** of the image..

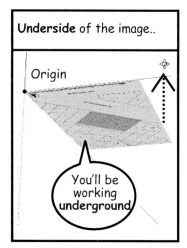

Origin

You'll be working **underground**

---

*The image **darkens** as its **orientation** to the SketchUp light source **changes**

Add a **New Layer** for the model base...

To create the model base, **DRAG** a **Rectangle** over the **underside** of the plat map...

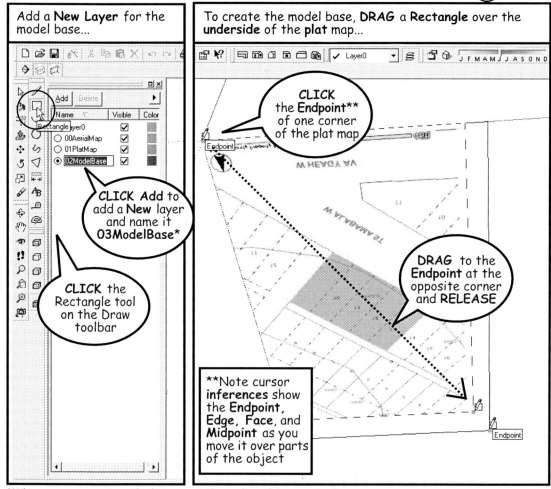

CLICK the Endpoint** of one corner of the plat map

DRAG to the Endpoint at the opposite corner and RELEASE

CLICK **Add** to add a **New** layer and name it **03ModelBase***

CLICK the Rectangle tool on the Draw toolbar

**Note cursor **inferences** show the **Endpoint, Edge, Face**, and **Midpoint** as you move it over parts of the object

*When you use a number, the layers sort themselves alphanumerically

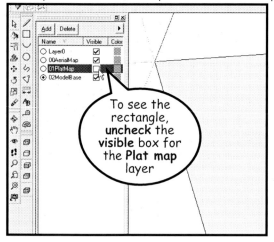

To see the rectangle, **uncheck** the **visible** box for the **Plat map** layer

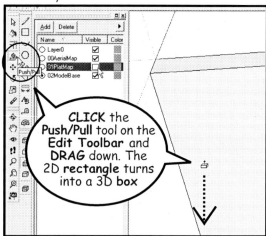

CLICK the **Push/Pull** tool on the **Edit Toolbar** and **DRAG** down. The 2D **rectangle** turns into a 3D **box**

## Extrude the Model Base

The **Push/Pull** tool extrudes a 2D object like a rectangle into a **3D object** like a **box**... The box becomes the **model base** and is now the same size as the **plat map**

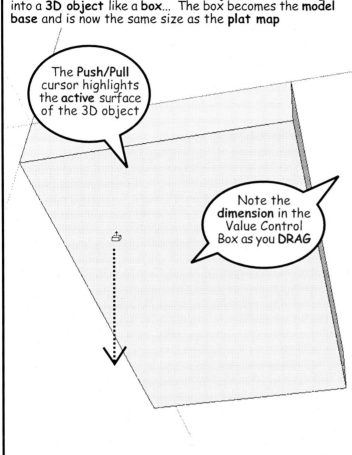

The **Push/Pull** cursor highlights the **active** surface of the 3D object

Note the **dimension** in the Value Control Box as you **DRAG**

As you **CLICK** and **DRAG** the surface downward. The length is displayed in the Value Control Box as you **DRAG**...

Distance 30' 4 1/2"

You can **DRAG** the Push/Pull tool to a dimension or **KEY IN** the distance **directly** from the keyboard...

No need to **CLICK**

Distance 50'

Don't forget to **Save**, just in case the **program crashes**... they all do...

**CLICK SAVE**

You might also use the **Save As** feature to **save** a copy under a **different name**, just in case

---

Make the 3D base **transparent** so you can see the future excavation and foundation

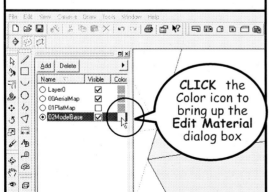

**CLICK** the Color icon to bring up the **Edit Material** dialog box

---

The **Edit Material** dialog box adds colors that make the model more **realistic**...

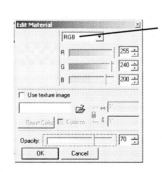

1. Select the **RGB** color palette

2. Set **color** values to R=255/G=240/B=200*

3. Change the transparency to **70%**

17

*You can **DOUBLE CLICK** the number and KEY IN new values directly without scrolling them in...

A **Left** to **Right** selection box selects all the pieces **within** the box

The **Left/Right DRAG** selects **lines** and **surfaces** within the **field** of objects

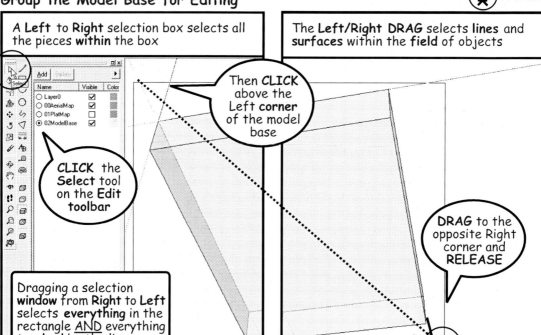

Then **CLICK** above the Left **corner** of the model base

**CLICK** the **Select** tool on the **Edit** toolbar

**DRAG** to the opposite Right corner and **RELEASE**

Dragging a selection **window** from **Right** to **Left** selects **everything** in the rectangle <u>AND</u> everything **touched** by the lines

---

The lines and surfaces of the model base are **separate** and must be **grouped**

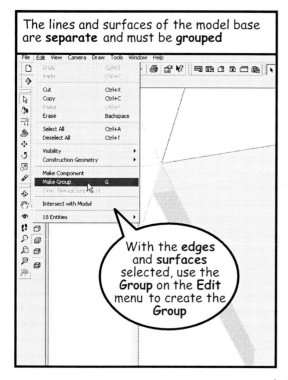

With the **edges** and **surfaces** selected, use the **Group** on the **Edit** menu to create the **Group**

As a **Group** the model base becomes a **"solid"** object and a **separate piece** of the model

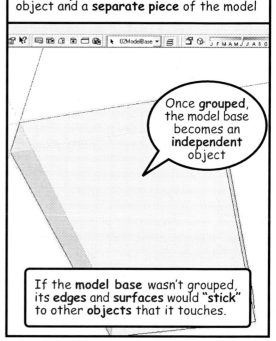

Once **grouped**, the model base becomes an **independent** object

If the **model base** wasn't grouped, its **edges** and **surfaces** would **"stick"** to other **objects** that it touches.

V15Base

CLICK the **visibility** icon to make the **Plat** layer visible

The model base is a separate piece of the final model* and **independent** of the plat map because the plat is a JPEG

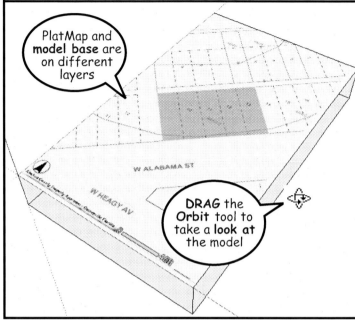

PlatMap and **model base** are on different layers

W ALABAMA ST

W HEACY AV

DRAG the **Orbit** tool to take a **look at** the model

*Isolating objects is critical in building a construction model...

CLICK SAVE

How did you do for time?

**20 minutes** (the first time...;-)

020

SAVE YOUR MINUTES

(Remember to close the program when not in use)

READY

OK, let's go to **STEP02**

### DO YOU KNOW HOW TO:

1. Transfer an image to your hard-drive
2. Create layers and control their visibility
3. Insert an image file into SketchUp
4. View a model from different angles
5. Size an image file to the real world
6. Draw a 2D rectangle using inferences
7. Extrude a 2D shape into a 3D object
8. Group the 3D object into a solid object
9. Change layer color and transparency
10. Select and Orbit objects in 3D

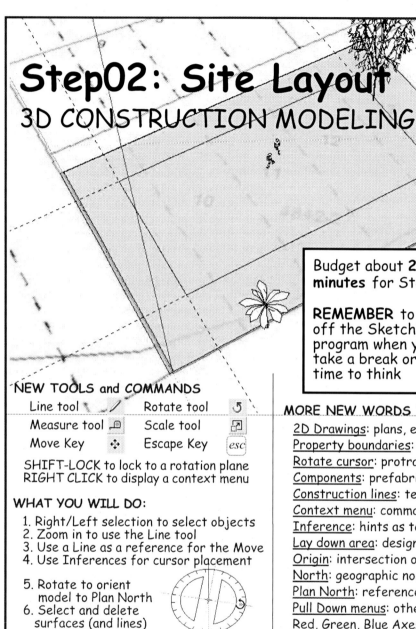

# Step02: Site Layout
## 3D CONSTRUCTION MODELING

Budget about **25 minutes** for Step02.

**REMEMBER** to turn off the SketchUp program when you take a break or need time to think

020

### NEW TOOLS and COMMANDS

| | | | |
|---|---|---|---|
| Line tool | / | Rotate tool | 5 |
| Measure tool | 🔎 | Scale tool | ⊡ |
| Move Key | ✛ | Escape Key | esc |

SHIFT-LOCK to lock to a rotation plane
RIGHT CLICK to display a context menu

### WHAT YOU WILL DO:

1. Right/Left selection to select objects
2. Zoom in to use the Line tool
3. Use a Line as a reference for the Move
4. Use Inferences for cursor placement
5. Rotate to orient model to Plan North
6. Select and delete surfaces (and lines)
7. Drag Construction lines for setbacks
8. Right-Click to view Context Menus
9. Insert and place Components
10. Resize Components as necessary

### MORE NEW WORDS TO REVIEW

2D Drawings: plans, elevations, sections
Property boundaries: limits of site
Rotate cursor: protractor on Rotate tool
Components: prefabricated model objects
Construction lines: temporary layout lines
Context menu: command or object menu
Inference: hints as to cursor location
Lay down area: designated work area
Origin: intersection of 3 axes
North: geographic north on a survey
Plan North: reference north on a plan
Pull Down menus: other menu options
Red, Green, Blue Axes: X, Y, and Z axes
Right/Left: selects everything touched
Setbacks: limits of construction
Shift Lock: constrains a tool to a plane
Surface: surface separate from edges
Transparent: used with other active tools
Sense of scale: helps visualize the model

When temporarily **Grouped** the model **base** and **plat** map can be moved **together**

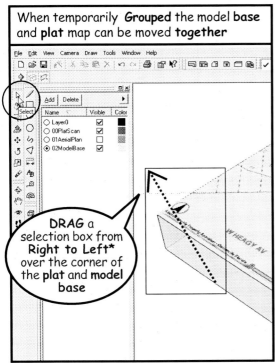

DRAG a selection box from **Right to Left*** over the corner of the **plat** and **model base**

A **Group** combines two separate **objects** or **Groups** so they act as a **single unit**

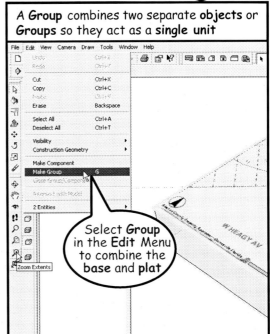

Select **Group** in the **Edit** Menu to combine the **base** and **plat**

*When dragging from **Right to Left**, everything the box touches is selected

Understanding the extent of the **site** is the **first step** in **any** construction

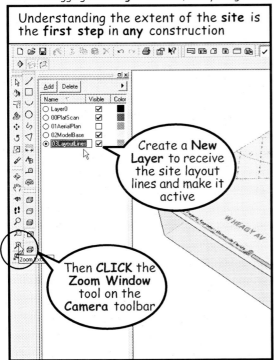

Create a **New Layer** to receive the site layout lines and make it active

Then **CLICK** the **Zoom Window** tool on the **Camera** toolbar

The **Zoom Window** tool moves in **closer** to focus on a particular **part** of the **model**

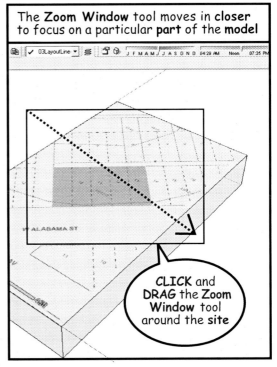

**CLICK** and **DRAG** the **Zoom Window** tool around the **site**

# Align the Site to the Origin

A line along the **approximate*** property line on the **plat map** acts as a **layout line**

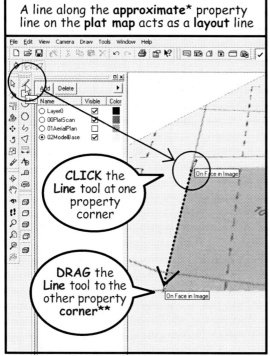

CLICK the **Line** tool at one property corner

DRAG the **Line** tool to the other property **corner****

The **layout line** can now be **grouped** to the **model base** group to **keep** them **together**

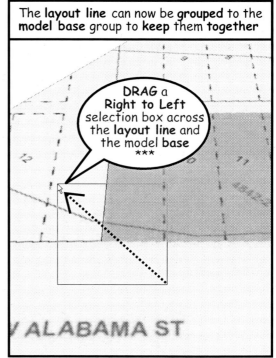

DRAG a **Right to Left** selection box across the **layout line** and the model **base** ***

*Approximate lengths and alignments are close enough for model building

With the **layout line** and model **base** group selected, the end of the line at the property **corner** acts as a **handle** to move the group to the **Origin** point and rotate it to **North**

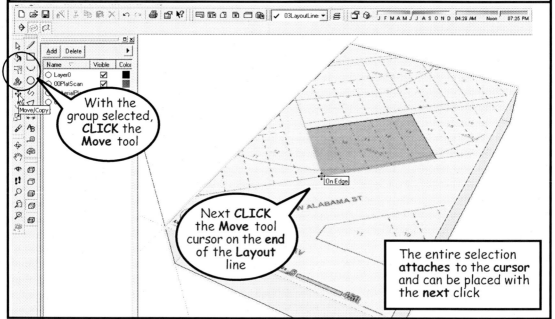

With the group selected, **CLICK** the **Move** tool

Next CLICK the **Move** tool cursor on the **end** of the **Layout** line

The entire selection **attaches** to the **cursor** and can be placed with the **next** click

**Use the Escape Key or click the Select tool to terminate the Line command

***The Right to Left selection box selects both the line and plat/model base Group

# Orient the Site to North

The **Move** tool places the south **property corner** at the **Origin** of the **SketchUp** axes

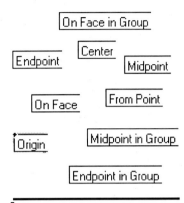

CLICK the **Endpoint** of the layout line to the **Origin**

**Inference** clues give different colored **reference** lines and cursor location for many **Edit** and **Draw** tools.

On Face in Group

Center

Endpoint

Midpoint

On Face

From Point

Origin

Midpoint in Group

Endpoint in Group

Use the **Escape Key** if you **CLICK** too soon, in the wrong place, or just want to **start over**.

esc

---

Once the **property corner** is placed at the **Origin**, you can **rotate** the grouped model **base** to the **North axis**

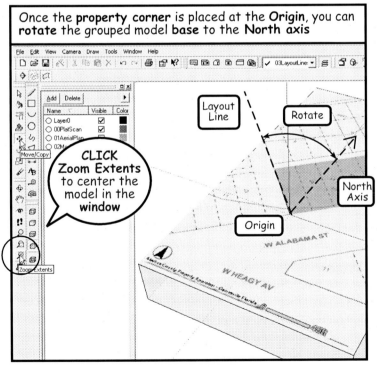

CLICK **Zoom Extents** to center the model in the window

Layout Line

Rotate

North Axis

Origin

---

The model **axes oriented** to the SketchUp **axes***

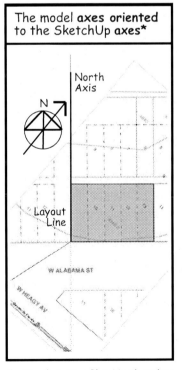

North Axis

Layout Line

---

23

*Orienting to the North Axis or **Plan North** makes it easier to build and display the model

V21Orient

**CLICK SAVE**

Time check: figure **5 minutes** to complete the Group and Move (**the first time**)

025

Use the **Edit>Select All** menu to make sure **everything** is selected

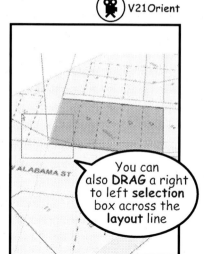

You can also **DRAG** a right to left **selection** box across the **layout** line

W ALABAMA ST

With everything selected **CLICK** the **Rotate** tool on the **Edit** toolbar

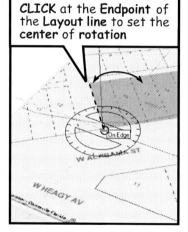

**CLICK** at the **Endpoint** of the **Layout line** to set the **center** of rotation

On Edge

W ALABAMA ST

W HEAGY AV

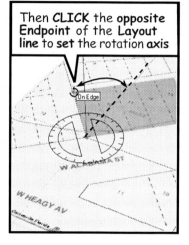

Then **CLICK** the **opposite Endpoint** of the **Layout line** to **set** the rotation **axis**

On Edge

W ALABAMA ST

W HEAGY AV

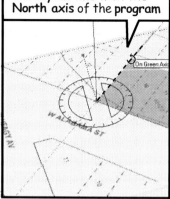

**Rotate** the compass to **align** the **layout line** with the **North axis** of the **program**

On Green Axis

W ALABAMA ST

**Pan** or **Zoom** to increase accuracy when (really) necessary

The tools on the **Camera** toolbar are "transparent" and can be used while other tools are **active**. RightClick to **Exit**

Try it: with the **Rotate** tool still active **CLICK** the Zoom **Window** tool and **DRAG** a box around the **Origin** of the SketchUp axes.

Note that the **active** tool returns immediately after you complete the box.

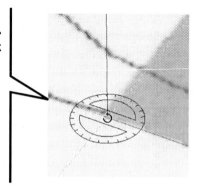

24

# Setup the Site Boundaries

V25Layout

Property lines are the **limits** of construction

To **quickly lay out** the property lines use the **rectangle** tool to draw lines on all **four sides** of the site

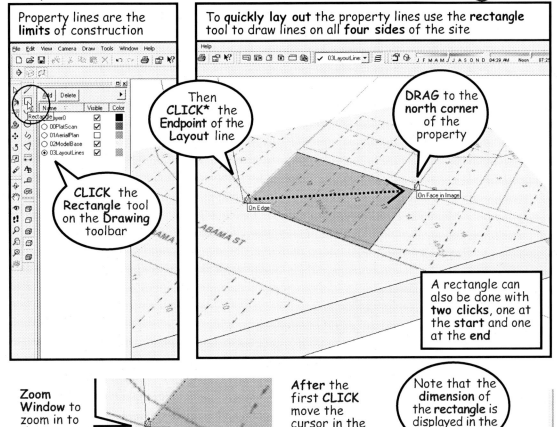

Then **CLICK\*** the **Endpoint** of the **Layout** line

**DRAG** to the **north corner** of the property

**CLICK** the **Rectangle** tool on the **Drawing** toolbar

A rectangle can also be done with **two clicks**, one at the **start** and one at the **end**

**Zoom Window** to zoom in to the **property corner**

**After** the first **CLICK** move the cursor in the **direction** of the **other** property **corner**

Note that the **dimension** of the **rectangle** is displayed in the **value box**

Dimensions 60' 9 15/16", 39' 9 9/1

As you **move** the cursor, **KEY IN** the X,Y dimensions directly from the **keyboard**. The **rectangle** will draw **automatically**.

125' , 82'

Use an **apostrophe** for feet and a **comma** to separate the **dimensions**

If you **CLICK** again by accident and see a rectangle, **Undo and try again**

Dimensions 125',82'

\*See the 2D construction drawings

25

# Setup the Site Setback

The **Surface** of the **rectangle** is separate from its edges and acts **independently**

SELECT the **surface** of the rectangle and **not** the edges

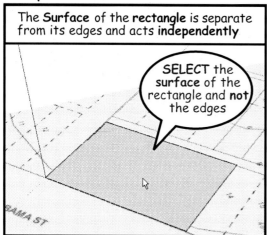

Press the **Delete** key with the **surface** selected

Once the **surface** is deleted the property lines **remain** in the model

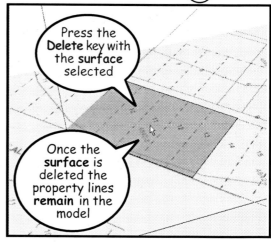

---

The **Measure** tool creates **construction lines**

First CLICK the Measure tool

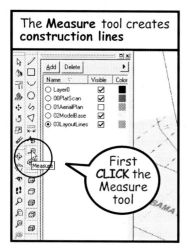

The **construction lines** are drawn on the **current layer**

CLICK the west line and **DRAG** to the east

KEY IN the 15' setback

15'

Length 15'

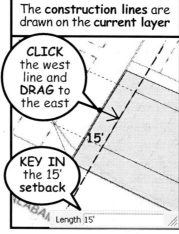

**Construction lines** extend to the **edge** of model **space**

DRAG and **KEY IN** another line **from the east**

15'

Length 15'

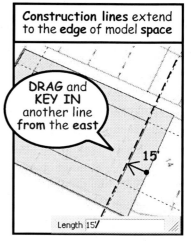

---

The **setback lines** represent the **limits** of the completed **structure** and should be **clearly** located **before** construction

15'

25'

Add **front** and **rear** setbacks

**Construction lines** are special SketchUp objects.

**RIGHT CLICK** the **line** to bring up a **context menu** to Hide, Erase, or Entity Info

Entity Info
Erase     Backspace
Hide

CLICK SAVE

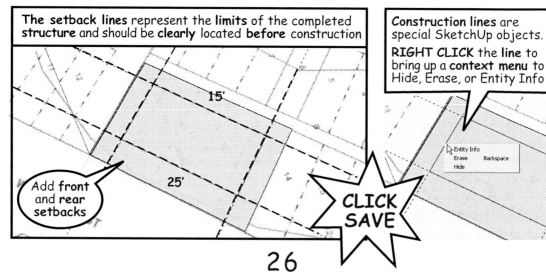

26

# Populate the Site for Visual Scale

**Create a new layer named "Populate" for components**

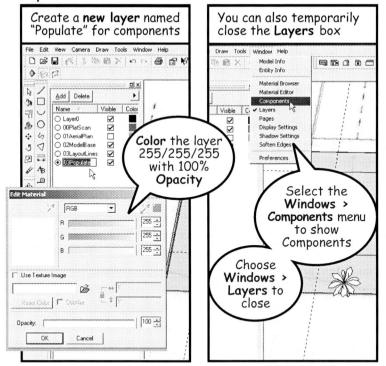

Color the layer 255/255/255 with 100% **Opacity**

**You can also temporarily close the Layers box**

Select the **Windows > Components** menu to show Components

Choose **Windows > Layers** to close

**Components are prefabricated models**

**DOUBLE CLICK** the folder to view

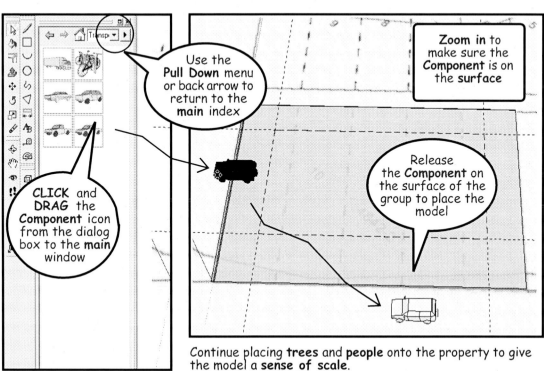

Use the **Pull Down** menu or back arrow to return to the **main** index

**CLICK** and **DRAG** the **Component** icon from the dialog box to the **main** window

**Zoom in** to make sure the **Component** is on the **surface**

Release the **Component** on the surface of the group to place the model

Continue placing **trees** and **people** onto the property to give the model a **sense of scale**.

# Scale Trees to Site Conditions

The **size** of Components can also be **changed**

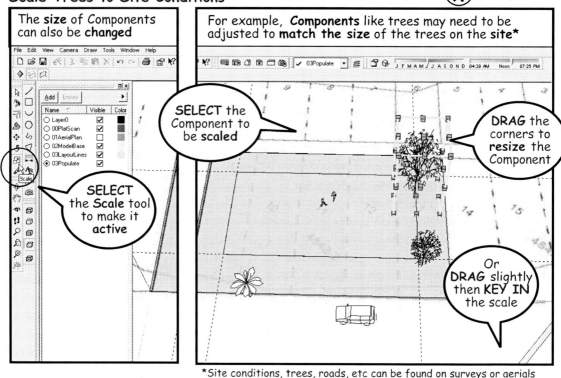

For example, **Components** like trees may need to be adjusted to **match the size** of the trees on the site*

*SELECT the Component to be scaled*

*SELECT the Scale tool to make it active*

*DRAG the corners to resize the Component*

*Or DRAG slightly then KEY IN the scale*

*Site conditions, trees, roads, etc can be found on surveys or aerials

## DO YOU KNOW HOW TO:

1. Select objects from Right to Left to Group
2. Use the Zoom Window tool for close up work
3. Use the Line tool to draw a reference line
4. Use the Move tool to reposition objects
5. Use Inferences like Endpoint, Origin, etc
6. Rotate the construction site to Plan North
7. Use Select All to select everything in the model
8. Key In dimensions directly from the keyboard
9. Select and delete surfaces (and lines)
10. Drag out Construction lines with the Measure tool
11. Right-Click objects to view Context Menus
12. Insert and place Components
13. Adjust the Scale of a Component

**How's your time??**
25 minutes max for Step02,
**45min** total so far, **right?**

CLICK SAVE

(Remember to close the program when not in use)

READY

OK, let's go to STEP03

# Step03: Work Plan
## 3D CONSTRUCTION MODELING

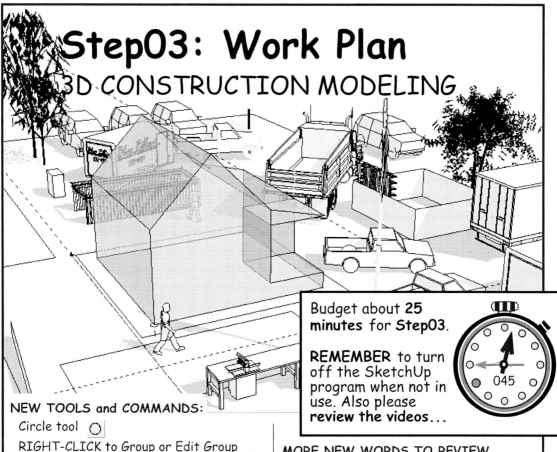

Budget about **25 minutes** for **Step03**.

**REMEMBER** to turn off the SketchUp program when not in use. Also please **review the videos...**

045

**NEW TOOLS and COMMANDS:**

Circle tool ◯

RIGHT-CLICK to Group or Edit Group
Hide/Unhide objects
Shift-CLICK to select

**WHAT YOU WILL DO:**

1. Use Orbit and Pan to view the model
2. Layout with the Measure tool

3. Set up the construction Workpoint
4. Use Circle to mark the Workpoint

5. Set up a "footprint" layer
6. Build a massing model
7. Use the model to visualize construction

7. View the site from different angles
9. Develop a work plan

**MORE NEW WORDS TO REVIEW**

<u>2D Footprint</u>: the perimeter of the building
<u>3D Footprint</u>: a building massing model
<u>3D Axes</u>: Red, Green, Blue (X,Y,Z) axes
<u>Drainage plan</u>: protects adjacent property
<u>Eave</u>: The lower overhang of the roof slope
<u>Laydown area</u>: prep and measure area
<u>Massing model</u>: 3D outline of building shape
<u>Ridge</u>: the high point of a roof
<u>SUP</u>: site utilization plan or work plan
<u>Staging area</u>: prefab or preassembly area
<u>Stringlines</u>: layout lines for construction
<u>Temporary power</u>: construction utilities
<u>Valley</u>: the inside angle of a slope change
<u>Workpoint</u>: reference point for the work

# Layout a Workpoint

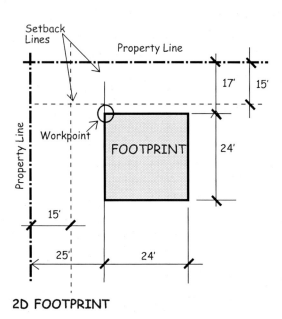

2D FOOTPRINT

The **Setback** lines can now be used to **layout** "stringlines" for the virtual construction

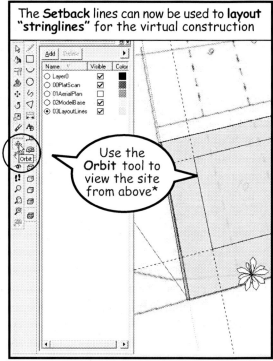

Use the **Orbit** tool to view the site from above*

*The Shift Key toggles the Orbit and Pan tool

**Construction** starts with a reference **workpoint**

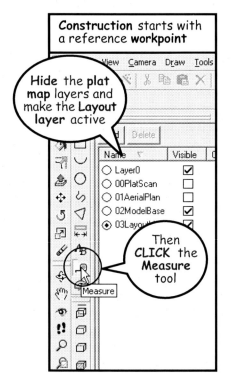

Hide the **plat map** layers and make the **Layout layer** active

Then CLICK the **Measure** tool

Review the 2D drawings to **find** the **dimensions** and **location** of the **workpoint** for the construction.

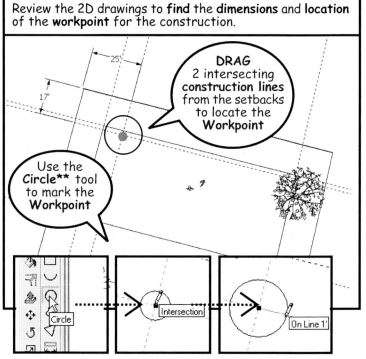

DRAG 2 intersecting **construction lines** from the setbacks to locate the **Workpoint**

Use the **Circle**** tool to mark the **Workpoint**

30

**CLICK and Delete the circle surface after the circle has been drawn

# Block Out a Massing Model

V31FootPrint

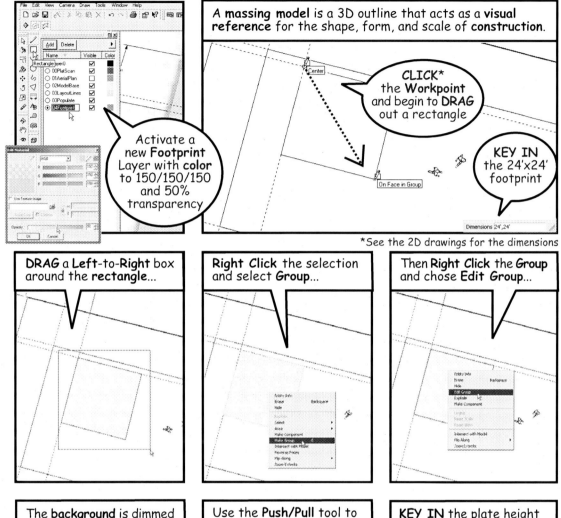

A **massing model** is a 3D outline that acts as a **visual reference** for the shape, form, and scale of **construction**.

Activate a new **Footprint** Layer with **color** to 150/150/150 and 50% transparency

CLICK* the **Workpoint** and begin to **DRAG** out a rectangle

KEY IN the 24'x24' footprint

*See the 2D drawings for the dimensions

**DRAG** a **Left**-to-**Right** box around the **rectangle**...

**Right Click** the selection and select **Group**...

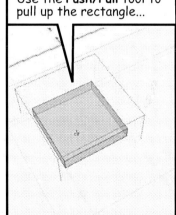

Then **Right Click** the **Group** and chose **Edit Group**...

The **background** is dimmed automatically for **editing**...

Use the **Push/Pull** tool to pull up the rectangle...

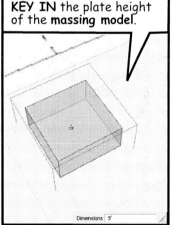

KEY IN the plate height of the **massing model**.

31

*The surface of the circle will intefere with the selection if it was not deleted

# Shape the Massing Model

**DRAG** the **Rectangle** tool to outline the **entry** area

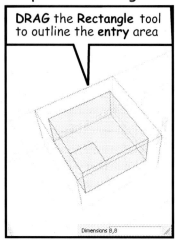

Use the **Push/Pull** tool to push **down** the entry deck

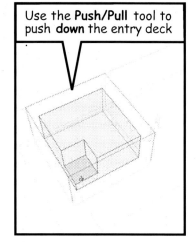

**Key In** the dimension to the top of the **entry** deck

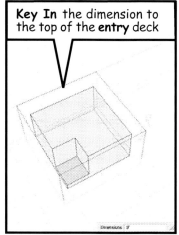

Use the **Line** tool to mark the roof **valley**...

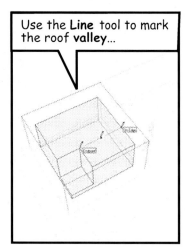

Use the **Line** tool again to mark the **ridge** line...

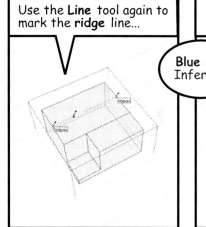

Pull the **ridge** up the axis with the **Move/Copy** tool...

Blue Axis Inference

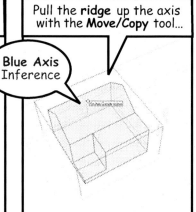

Move the **eave** down the blue axis with **Move/Copy**...

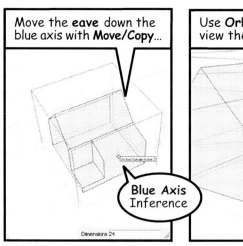

Blue Axis Inference

Use **Orbit** and **Zoom** to view the porch roof...

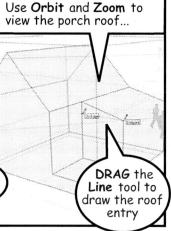

**DRAG** the **Line** tool to draw the roof entry

**Extrude** the triangular outline to form the roof

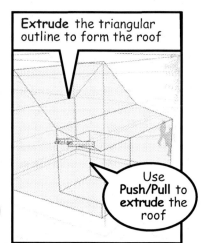

Use **Push/Pull** to **extrude** the roof

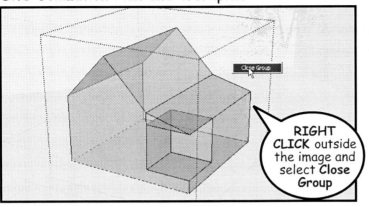

> RIGHT CLICK outside the image and select **Close Group**

**CLICK SAVE**

Time check: figure **15 minutes** to get to this point (**the first time**)

060

The **3D footprint** gives a rough idea of the **extent** of **construction** and can be used to **visualize the** work

**Unhide** layers and set up a **new layer** called SUP for the **workplan***

You can use **Orbit, Pan,** and **Zoom** tools to visualize **the work** from different points of view. **Review** the 2D plans and **think** through the **construction process**...

> Unhide the Plat layer

> Activate a new SUP layer and set RGB colors to 255/255/255 (**White**)

> What's the most **efficient way** to use the job site? Materials, labor, equipment, safety, access, etc?

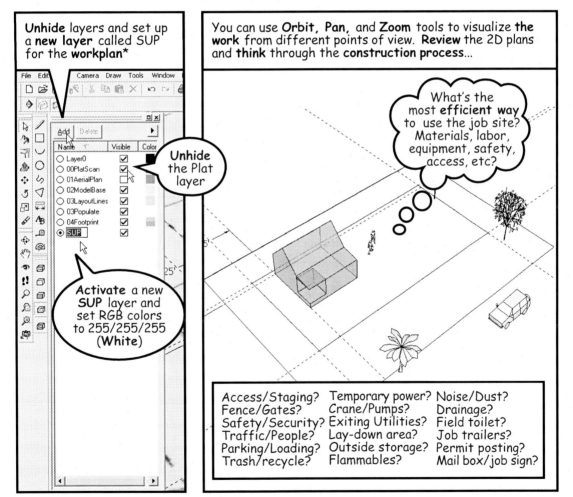

| | | |
|---|---|---|
| Access/Staging? | Temporary power? | Noise/Dust? |
| Fence/Gates? | Crane/Pumps? | Drainage? |
| Safety/Security? | Exiting Utilities? | Field toilet? |
| Traffic/People? | Lay-down area? | Job trailers? |
| Parking/Loading? | Outside storage? | Permit posting? |
| Trash/recycle? | Flammables? | Mail box/job sign? |

*SUP is a Site Utilization Plan or a work plan for the best way to use the site during construction

33

# Site Utilization Plan and Workplan

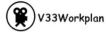 

A **workplan** starts with getting a **feel** for the site during the **preconstruction**. It's like visiting the site as a virtual **walk through** and determine the best way to **organize** the construction

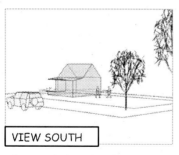

VIEW SOUTH

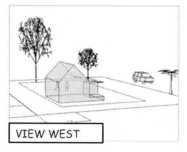

VIEW WEST

VIEW NORTH

The **workplan** should **simulate** the construction process: placing materials in storage, using lay down areas, and setting up equipment. It's **important** to think through the **sequence** of **construction** and the **flow** of labor and materials for **every phase** of the construction.

> Where's the best place to access, enter and exit the site?
>
> Where is a good unloading and storage area?
>
> Efficient placement of trash and temporary utilities?
>
> Laydown and staging areas close to temporary power?
>
> Are there safety or security problems?
>
> Will traffic or pedestrian controls be necessary?
>
> Where do employees take a break, park, go to the bathroom?

A preliminary **workplan for** this **jobsite** might look like this:

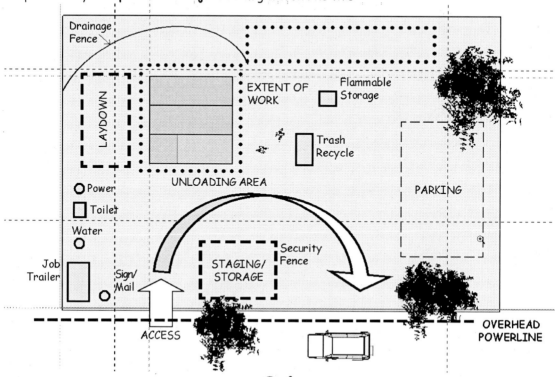

34

 V33Workplan

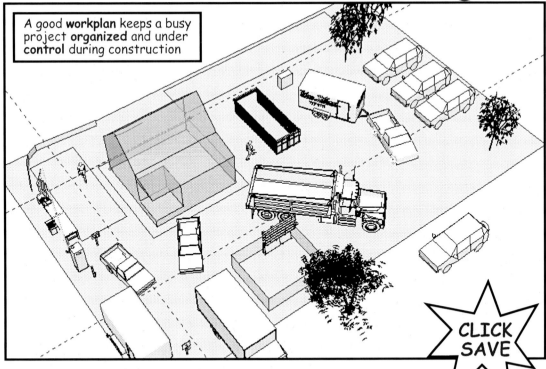

A good **workplan** keeps a busy project **organized** and under **control** during construction

**CLICK SAVE**

How did you do for time?

**25 minutes** to complete Step03

070

**SAVE YOUR MINUTES**

(Remember to **close the program** when not in use)

Components from the **SketchUp Forum** by David Mihm, John Yurko, and Archutek. The **Forum** is on the **SketchUp Website** and contains discussion areas, materials, and a gallery.

## DO YOU KNOW HOW TO:

1. Create layers and adjust color and transparency
2. Orbit, Pan and Zoom to change points of view
3. Use the Measure tool to draw construction lines
4. Use a Left/Right vs Right/Left selection box
5. RIGHT-CLICK a selection to create a Group
6. RIGHT-CLICK a Group to Edit the group
7. Shape the massing model with Line and Move tools
8. Shape the model using Rectangle and Push/Pull
9. Use the model to visualize the work process

**READY**

**OK**, let's go to **STEP04**

# Step04: Excavation
## 3D CONSTRUCTION MODELING

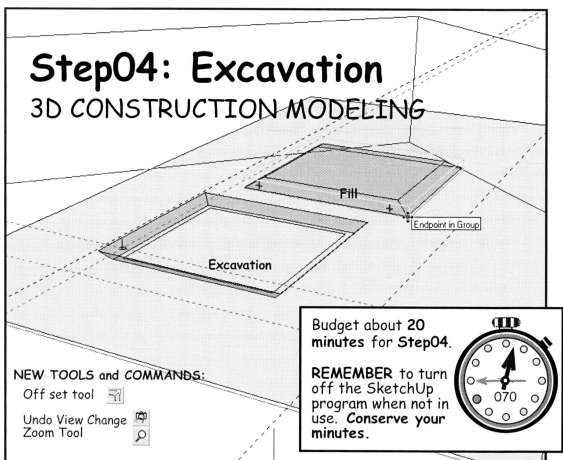

Fill

Excavation

Endpoint in Group

Budget about **20 minutes** for **Step04.**

**REMEMBER** to turn off the SketchUp program when not in use. **Conserve your minutes.**

070

## NEW TOOLS and COMMANDS:

Off set tool

Undo View Change
Zoom Tool

## WHAT YOU WILL DO:

1. Hide layers and zoom to the workpoint
2. Draw a survey stake as a reference
3. Height of stake is depth of excavation

4. Use Undo View Change to Zoom out
5. Right Click to edit the model base group
6. Zoom back to the Workpoint

7. DRAG a rectangle on the model base for the cut
8. Key In the dimensions for the excavation
9. Zoom out and select the rectangle

10. Use the Offset tool to layout cuts
11. Push/Pull to shape the excavation

## MORE NEW WORDS TO REVIEW:

Angle of repose: slope of the cut in earth
Backfill: the material that fills an excavation
Excavation: earth removed for foundation
Footing: a foundation bearing member
Foundation: footing, wall, and slab
Morph: transform from flat to excavated
Perimeter: outside face of foundation wall
Survey Stake: reference set by surveyor
Toe of slope: bottom of the cut in earth
Top of slope: top of the cut in earth
Vertical reference: to changes in elevation
Visibility: Hide or unhide layers for work
Workpoint: construction reference point

# Set a Survey Stake at the Workpoint

Change layer **visibility** for the **excavation**...

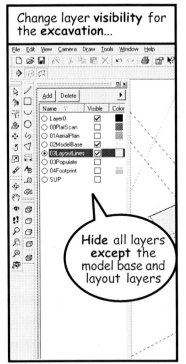

*Hide* all layers **except** the model base and layout layers

Set a **vertical** reference for the depth of the **excavation** at the base of the **workpoint** as a survey stake

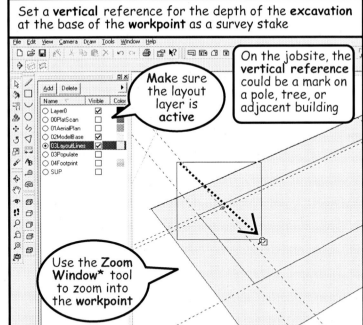

On the jobsite, the **vertical reference** could be a mark on a pole, tree, or adjacent building

Make sure the layout layer is **active**

Use the **Zoom Window\*** tool to zoom into the **workpoint**

*Zoom tools are transparent and can be used during an active command

---

The **excavation** depth is the **bottom** of the footing

**CLICK** the Line tool and **draw** a vertical line up the blue axis\*\*

On Blue Axis 2'

**KEY IN** the height\*\*\* of the stake (same as the **depth** of the **excavation**)

After placing the **stake** as a reference at the **workpoint**, you can **edit** the **model base** to start the **excavation**

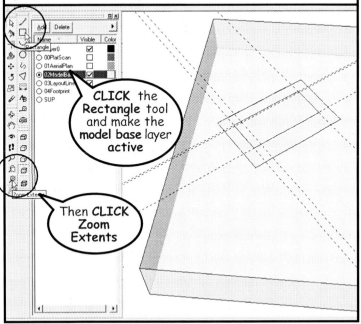

**CLICK** the Rectangle tool and make the **model base** layer active

Then **CLICK** Zoom Extents

\*\*Use the Escape Key or click the Select tool to terminate the Line command

\*\*\*See the 2D drawings for the depth

## The **model base** should now be **visible** in the **window**

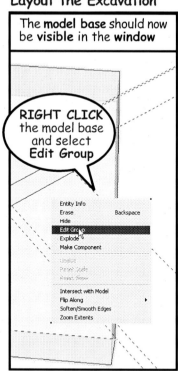

RIGHT CLICK the model base and select Edit Group

## Once in **Edit** Group, use Zoom Window to **zoom back** to the **workpoint** and layout the perimeter of the **stem wall***

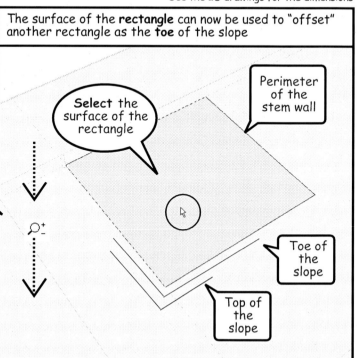

Use **Undo View Change** to zoom back to the **workpoint**

CLICK the **workpoint** with **Rectangle** tool and **DRAG** to the southeast

KEY IN the dimensions* as you **DRAG** the rectangle

*See the 2D drawings for the dimensions

## DRAG the **Zoom** tool to zoom out and **see** the **rectangle**

Use Zoom and **DRAG** downward to view all the **rectangle**

## The surface of the **rectangle** can now be used to "offset" another rectangle as the **toe** of the slope

**Select** the surface of the rectangle

Perimeter of the stem wall

Toe of the slope

Top of the slope

# Layout the Excavation

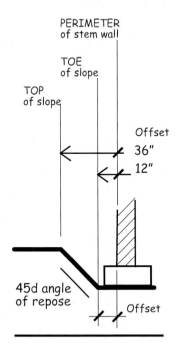

PERIMETER
of stem wall

TOE
of slope

TOP
of slope

Offset
36"
12"

45d angle
of repose

Offset

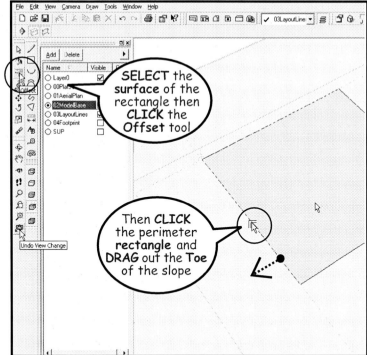

SELECT the **surface** of the rectangle then **CLICK** the **Offset** tool

Then **CLICK** the perimeter **rectangle** and **DRAG** out the **Toe** of the slope

Keep in mind the **model base** remains an **active** group and is still selected in the background and **open for editing**, so take care not to **Move** or **Delete** parts of the model base by mistake*

**CLICK SAVE**

Figure **5 minutes** max to **this stage** of the **Excavation**

075

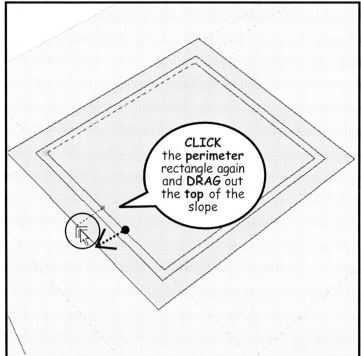

**CLICK** the **perimeter** rectangle again and **DRAG** out the **top** of the slope

*In SketchUp you can Undo all the way back to the last SAVE

39

 V38Excavate

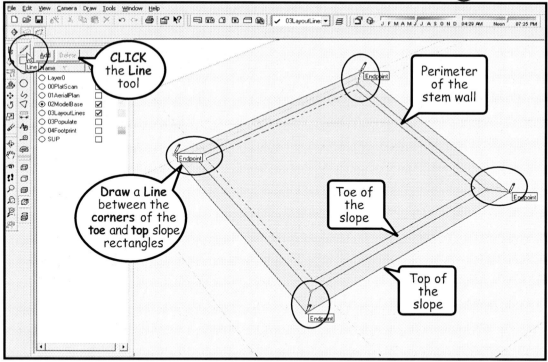

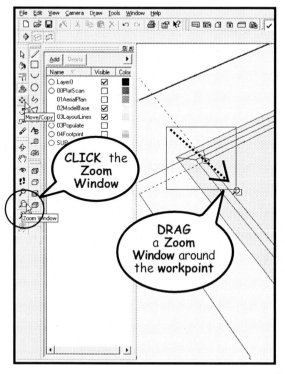

The **workpoint** and the **survey stake** are dim because only the surface of the model base is active in **Edit Group**...

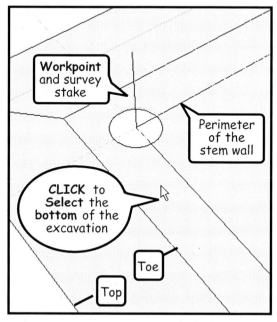

40

V38Excavate

When you **move** the selected **surface down** the **height** of the **stake**, the corner lines **morph** to the **sloping sides**

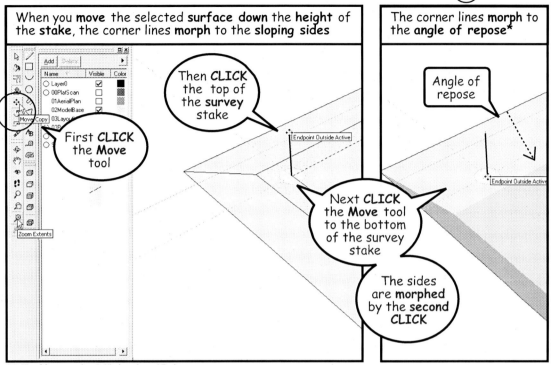

Then **CLICK** the top of the **survey stake**

First **CLICK** the **Move** tool

Next **CLICK** the **Move** tool to the bottom of the survey stake

The sides are **morphed** by the **second CLICK**

The corner lines **morph** to the **angle of repose***

Angle of repose

*24" offset and a 24" depth = 45 degrees

The **excavation** is now "cut" into the top **surface** of the model base.with a 45degree angle of repose*

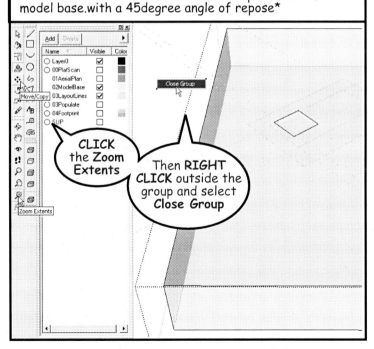

**CLICK** the **Zoom Extents**

Then **RIGHT CLICK** outside the group and select **Close Group**

CLICK SAVE

**20 minutes** for **Step04**
(If you're ahead of time, **try** the backfill)

090

(90 minutes total)
CONSERVE YOUR MINUTES

41

## Stockpile the Backfill

You can now **view** the excavation from **different angles** and make a **stockpile** of backfill next to the **excavation** in the model base. **To start make sure the Model base is not selected.**

---

1. **DRAG** a rectangle over the **top** of the excavation and then **Group** the rectangle

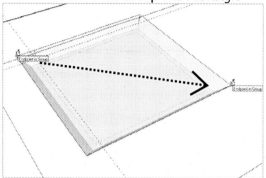

2. **Right CLICK** and edit the grouped **rectangle**. Then offset the edges. **Draw** the corner lines

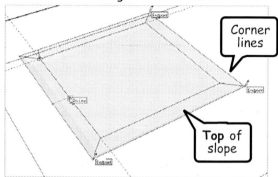

Corner lines

Top of slope

3. **SELECT** the top inside **surface of the rectangle** and use the **Move** tool to pull it up

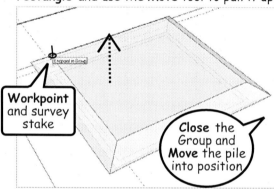

Workpoint and survey stake

Close the Group and Move the pile into position

### NOTE:

1. The height of **fill** is the height of the stake or "**depth**" of the excavation. In actual construction the shape and volume of the fill will be larger than the excavation because of soil fluff.

2. Use this **same method** to model a pile of fill, excavate a trench footing, or layout and dig more complex foundations:

  a. Edit the model base to layout the footprint
  b. Offset the top and toe of slopes
  c. Connect corners of the angle of repose
  d. Use the Move tool to shape the cut or fill

---

### DO YOU KNOW HOW TO:

1. Control the visibility of layers
2. Select and change active layers
3. Access a Group with Right Click
4. Zoom in to work on part of the model
5. Use Undo View Change to return to the previous view
6. Drag a Line or Rectangle and Key In dimensions
7. Use the Zoom tool to Drag in and out of a view
8. Use the Offset tool to create a parallel line
9. Morph a selected surface with the Move tool
10. Reverse the technique to pile up backfill

CLICK SAVE

READY

OK, let's go to **STEP05**

# Step05: Foundation
## 3D CONSTRUCTION MODELING

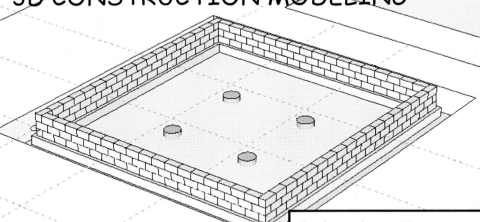

## NEW TOOLS and COMMANDS

CTRL CLICK to set an axis
CTRL DRAG to make multiple copies
HIDE an object

Make a Component from a Group
Edit Just This One component

Shift Constrain Move and copies

## WHAT YOU WILL DO

1. Draw a plumb-line to lower the workpoint
2. Set up a concrete layer for the footing
3. Draw a rectangle for the footing base

4. Set up a concrete block layer
5. Use a rectangle as
   a concrete block
6. CTRL DRAG copies
   of blocks as arrays

7. Group the arrays to build the wall

8. Simulate the sequence
   of construction
9. Build pier footings
   for bearing posts

Budget about **30 minutes** for Step05.

If you notice your computer slowing down, you may have insufficient memory for 3D modeling*.

090

## MORE NEW WORDS TO REVIEW

<u>Array</u>: circular or linear rows of copies
<u>Block</u>: 8x8x16 hollow concrete masonry unit
<u>Footing</u>: a continuous concrete bearing pad
<u>Footer</u>**: another word for a footing
<u>Component</u>: prefabricated piece of a model
<u>Half block</u>: a "split" or 8" x 8" x 8" block
<u>Hot spot</u>: active point of a cursor or object
<u>Perimeter</u>: the outside face of foundation
<u>Pier footing</u>: concrete foundation at pier
<u>Plumb-line</u>: line perpendicular to the horizon
<u>Protractor</u>: measures degrees of an angle
<u>Simulation</u>: representation of a process
<u>Solid object</u>: group of lines and surfaces
<u>Stem wall</u>:foundation wall built on a footing
<u>X-Number</u>: the number of multiple copies

*Check your OpenGL settings in Preferences and change to "Use Hardware Acceleration"

**In common usage, though considered by some to be the incorrect name for a "footing"

# Lower the Workpoint

The **excavation** cut into the **model base** is now ready for construction of the **footing** and concrete block **stem wall**

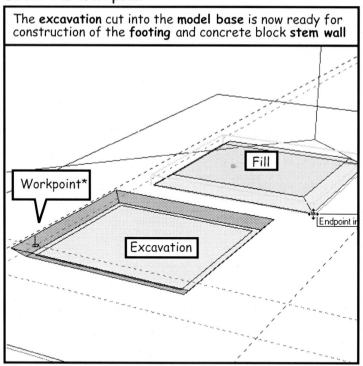

Fill

Workpoint*

Excavation

Endpoint in

The **Workpoint** is a layout reference for the site

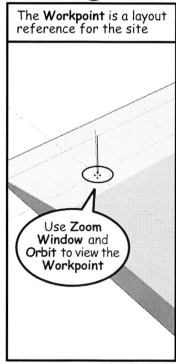

Use **Zoom Window** and **Orbit** to view the **Workpoint**

*The **Workpoint** is on the ground plane of the site (red/green plane)

Drop a plumb-line **down** from the **Workpoint**

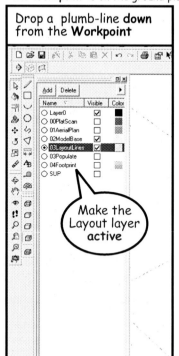

Make the Layout layer **active**

The **plumb-line** marks the corner of the perimeter of the stem wall at the bottom of the **excavation**

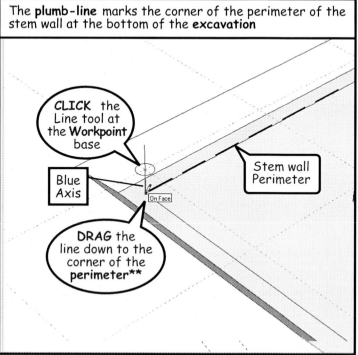

CLICK the Line tool at the **Workpoint** base

Blue Axis

On Face

Stem wall Perimeter

DRAG the line down to the corner of the **perimeter****

44

**Use the Escape Key or click the Select tool to terminate the Line command

# Layout the Footing

Create a new **concrete** layer for the **concrete** footing for the **foundation** wall

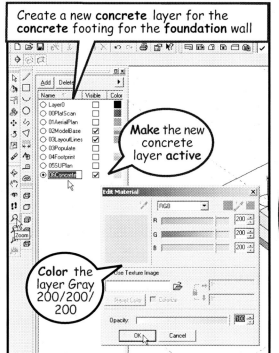

Make the new concrete layer **active**

Color the layer Gray 200/200/200

To reorient your point of view, use the **Zoom** and **Orbit** tools on the **Camera** toolbar

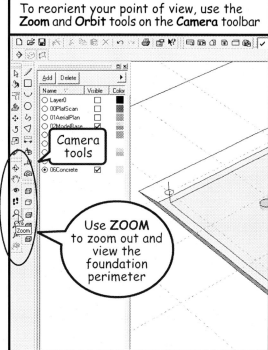

Camera tools

Use **ZOOM** to zoom out and view the foundation perimeter

Create a **layout rectangle** that can be used to form the **footing** and **guide** construction of the stem wall

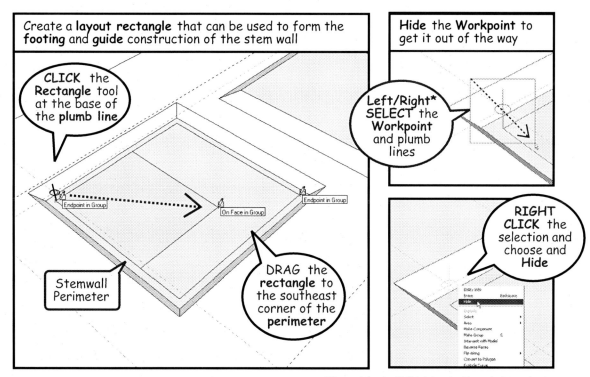

CLICK the **Rectangle** tool at the base of the **plumb line**

Stemwall Perimeter

DRAG the **rectangle** to the southeast corner of the **perimeter**

Hide the **Workpoint** to get it out of the way

Left/Right* SELECT the **Workpoint** and plumb lines

RIGHT CLICK the selection and choose and **Hide**

*Dragging a Left/Right selection window selects everything within the box

# Form the Footing

V44Footing

The **new** rectangle is the **same** dimension as the **perimeter** of the **stem wall**. The width will be **adjusted later**.

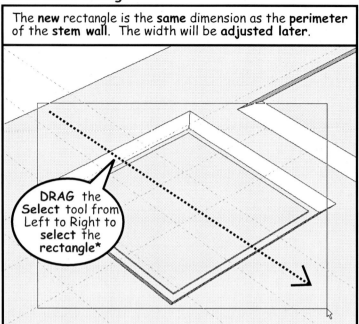

> DRAG the **Select** tool from Left to Right to **select** the rectangle*

*Make sure the model base is not selected

Once grouped the rectangle acts as a **horizontal reference** to build the concrete **footing** and layout the **concrete block** stem wall and concrete slab.

Build the **foundation model** following this process:

1. **Offset** the base of the footing inside the perimeter

2. **Pull up** the base to the height of the footing

3. **Fabricate** a concrete block and make it a **component**

4. Place **multiple copies** of the block as arrays

5. Build **groups of components** from these multiple copies

6. Stack the **groups** to form the foundation **stem walls**

6. **Pull out** the footing on four outer sides to complete the footing

---

**Groups** keep the pieces of the model separated in SketchUp as **solid objects**

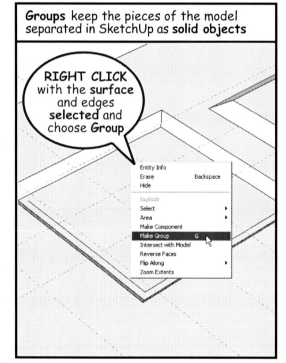

> RIGHT CLICK with the **surface** and edges **selected** and choose **Group**

---

Edit the **rectangle** with the **Offset** tool to form the **base** of the footing

> RIGHT CLICK and Edit Group

46

## Pour the Footing

The dimension of the **offset** is the width of the footing **inside** the wall perimeter*

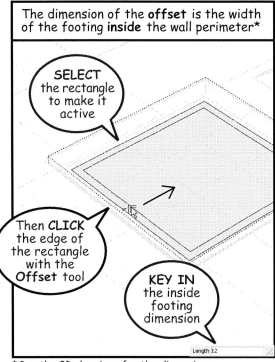

SELECT the rectangle to make it active

Then **CLICK** the edge of the rectangle with the **Offset** tool

KEY IN the inside footing dimension

Length 12

*See the 2D drawings for the dimensions

You **pour** the footing with the **Push/Pull** tool from the **bottom up**

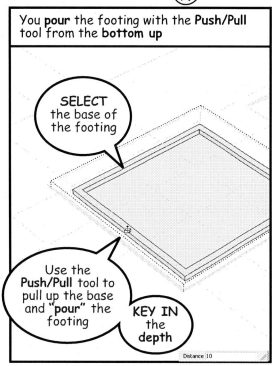

SELECT the base of the footing

Use the **Push/Pull** tool to pull up the base and "**pour**" the footing

KEY IN the **depth**

Distance 10

Once the **base** of the **footing** is created, the **inside** of the **rectangle** can be **deleted**

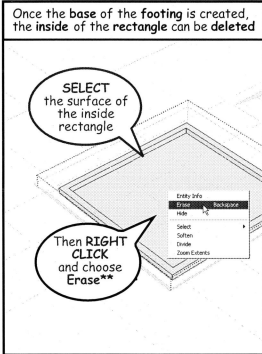

SELECT the surface of the inside rectangle

Entity Info
Erase          Backspace
Hide

Select
Soften
Divide
Zoom Extents

Then **RIGHT CLICK** and choose Erase**

The concrete **footing** is ready for the hollow masonry blocks of the **stem wall**

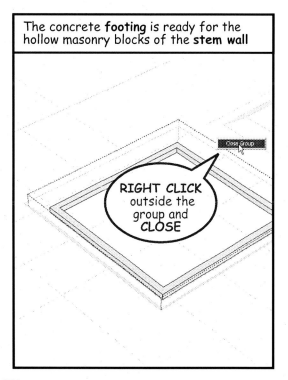

Close Group

**RIGHT CLICK** outside the group and **CLOSE**

**Or** select the surface and press **the Delete** or Backspace key

47

# Fabricate the Concrete Block

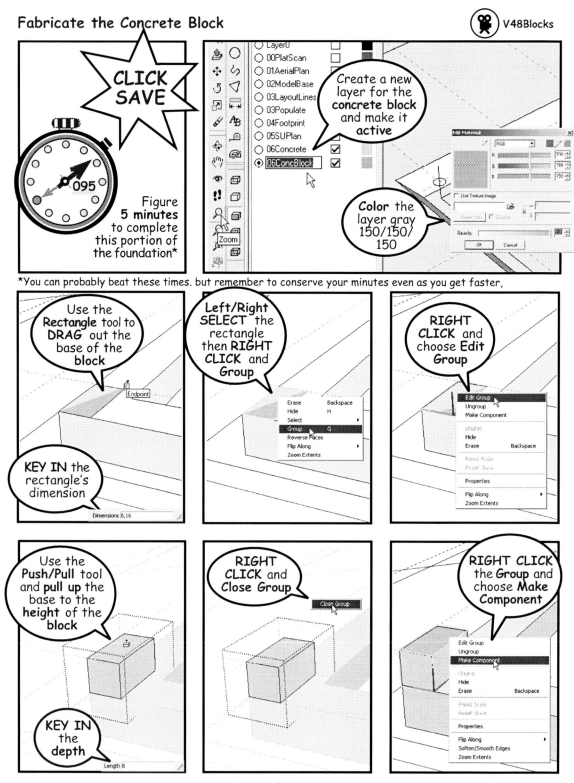

**CLICK SAVE**

095

Figure **5 minutes** to complete this portion of the foundation*

Create a new layer for the **concrete block** and make it **active**

LayerO
00PlatScan
01AerialPlan
02ModelBase
03LayoutLines
03Populate
04Footprint
05SUPlan
06Concrete  ☑
06ConcBlock  ☑

Color the layer gray 150/150/150

*You can probably beat these times. but remember to conserve your minutes even as you get faster,

Use the **Rectangle** tool to **DRAG** out the base of the block

Endpoint

**KEY IN** the rectangle's dimension

Dimensions 8,16

**Left/Right SELECT** the rectangle then **RIGHT CLICK** and **Group**

Erase        Backspace
Hide         H
Select       ▶
Group        G
Reverse Faces
Flip Along   ▶
Zoom Extents

**RIGHT CLICK** and choose **Edit Group**

Edit Group
Ungroup
Make Component

Explode
Hide
Erase        Backspace

Reset Scale
Reset Skew

Properties

Flip Along   ▶
Zoom Extents

Use the **Push/Pull** tool and **pull up** the base to the **height** of the block

**KEY IN** the **depth**

Length 8

**RIGHT CLICK** and **Close Group**

Close Group

**RIGHT CLICK** the **Group** and choose **Make Component**

Edit Group
Ungroup
Make Component

Explode
Hide
Erase        Backspace

Reset Scale
Reset Skew

Properties

Flip Along            ▶
Soften/Smooth Edges
Zoom Extents

48

# Stack the Concrete Blocks

 V48Blocks

Make a Group a **Component** whenever **more than one copy** of a Group will be used in a construction model. **Components** reduce demand on computer memory and **simplify** revisions.

Use the **Move** tool and **CTRL CLICK*** a corner of the component

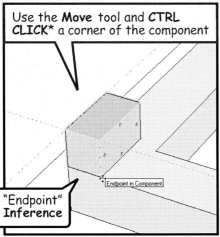

"Endpoint" Inference

*Endpoint in Component*

Hold the **CTRL Key** down as you **DRAG** the corner of the block

*On Face in Group*

"On Face" Inference

*Hold the Ctrl and Shift key and the drag/copy will be constrained in one direction

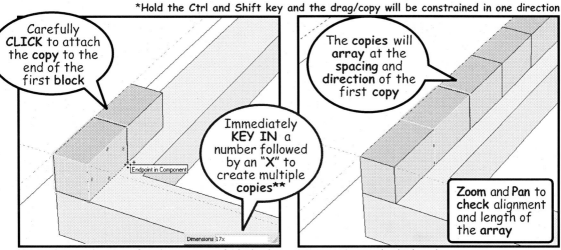

Carefully **CLICK** to attach the **copy** to the end of the first **block**

*Endpoint in Component*

Immediately **KEY IN** a number followed by an "X" to create multiple **copies****

*Dimensions :17x*

The **copies** will **array** at the **spacing** and **direction** of the first **copy**

**Zoom** and **Pan** to **check** alignment and length of the **array**

**See the 2D drawings for the number of blocks (or use any number and edit later)

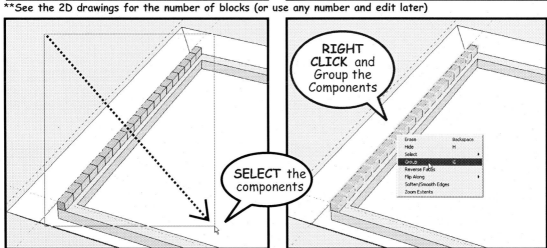

SELECT the components

RIGHT CLICK and Group the Components

| | |
|---|---|
| Erase | Backspace |
| Hide | H |
| Select | |
| Group | G |
| Reverse Faces | |
| Flip Along | |
| Soften/Smooth Edges | |
| Zoom Extents | |

## Rotate and Place the Concrete

When the protractor is aligned with an object's surface, hold the **Shift Key** down to **lock** the **rotation** to the plane of that surface (also works with other tools).

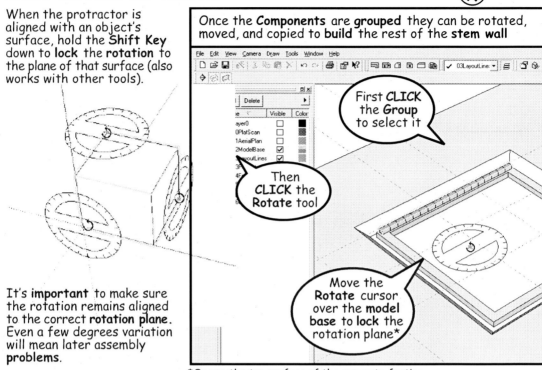

Once the **Components** are **grouped** they can be rotated, moved, and copied to **build** the rest of the **stem wall**

First **CLICK** the **Group** to select it

Then **CLICK** the **Rotate** tool

Move the **Rotate** cursor over the **model base** to **lock** the rotation plane*

It's **important** to make sure the rotation remains aligned to the correct **rotation plane.** Even a few degrees variation will mean later assembly **problems**.

*Or use the top surface of the concrete footing

Once you **have a lock**, hold the **Shift Key down** until you set the **axis** of the **rotation**.

**CLICK** the **Rotation** tool at the corner of the **group** to center the **axis** of **rotation**

CTRL CLICK the edge of the group to set the rotation **axis**

Once the axis is defined, use the **CTRL key** to make copies as you **ROTATE**

**CLICK** again to **place** the object on the **new** axis**

Use **Inferences** to keep the objects **aligned**

50

**You can also KEY IN the angle of rotation

V48Blocks

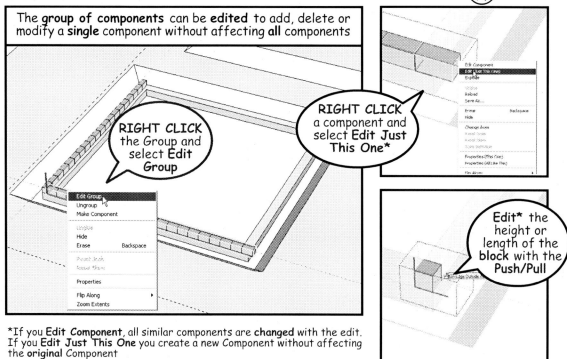

*If you **Edit Component**, all similar components are **changed** with the edit.
If you **Edit Just This One** you create a new Component without affecting
the **original** Component

**You can also press the Delete or Backspace key

51

***The point of selection is the point of placement

V52Stack

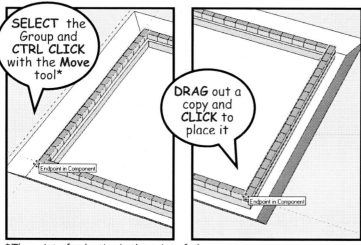

SELECT the Group and CTRL CLICK with the **Move** tool*

DRAG out a copy and CLICK to place it

Endpoint in Component

Endpoint in Component

*The point of selection is the point of placement

CLICK SAVE

105

Figure **15 more minutes** to complete this portion of the **foundation** wall

Once a **component** has been used once in a model, it can be **reinserted** at any time from the **component menu**

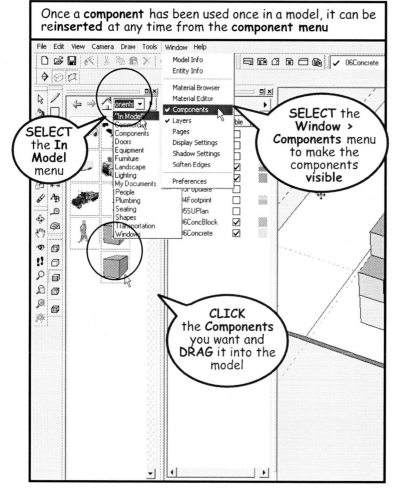

SELECT the **In Model** menu

SELECT the **Window > Components** menu to make the components **visible**

CLICK the **Components** you want and **DRAG** it into the model

The modeling process for the **next course** of the stem wall is the same as the first. You can lay down **entire rows** as groups of components or simulate the **real world** construction process: (See page 53)

1. **Insert** the component to start the course. Stagger placement at **midpoint** for a running bond

2. **CTRL CLICK** the component, then **DRAG** and **CLICK** to place a copy

3. **KEY IN** a number followed by an "X" to create an array of multiple **copies**

4. Use the **Rotate** tool to **rotate** a block and start the other side (or **Group** the line to rotate all at once)

5. **CTRL CLICK** to copy the rotation around the axis

6. **CTRL CLICK** to start a new line of multiple copies

7. You can **copy** the placement of blocks along the new wall

8. **Repeat** the block laying process to the **required height** of the wall. Blocks can be placed in **small groups** of Components or individually

## Laying the Block One by One

You can construct the **remainder** of the stem wall in the **same** way as the **first course**.

**Or** try laying the block one by one using the steps on Page 52 to **simulate** the **block laying** process,

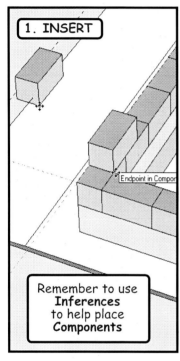

**1. INSERT**

Remember to use **Inferences** to help place **Components**

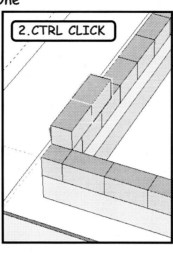

**2.CTRL CLICK**

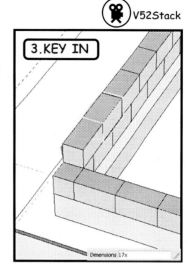

**3.KEY IN**

Dimensions 17x

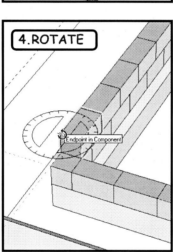

**4.ROTATE**

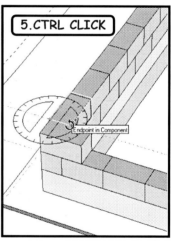

**5.CTRL CLICK**

**6.CTRL CLICK**

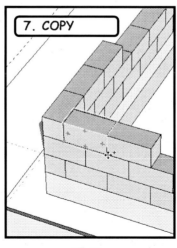

**7. COPY**

**8.REPEAT**

53

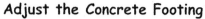

Zoom in and **pull out** the concrete footing on all **four sides** of the **perimeter**

Use **Zoom Window** and **Orbit** to view the **corner**

RIGHT-CLICK to Edit Group

Edit Group
Ungroup
Make Component

Unglue
Hide
Erase                    Backspace

Reset Scale
Reset Skew

Properties

Use **Push/Pull** tool to **extend** the footing

KEY IN the dimension

Distance 4

**CLICK SAVE**

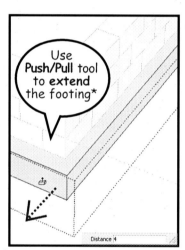

Use **Push/Pull** tool to **extend** the footing*

Distance 4

**Zoom** out and **Orbit** to extend the **footing** on all sides

*See the 2D drawings for the dimensions

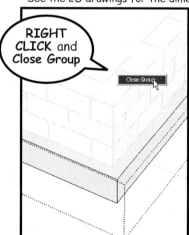

RIGHT CLICK and Close Group

Close Group

With the **stem wall and footing** complete, the **pier footings** can now be built**

**In actual construction, the perimeter and pier footings would be completed before the block wall

# Layout the Pier Footing

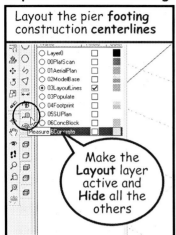

**Layout the pier footing construction centerlines**

Make the **Layout** layer active and **Hide** all the others

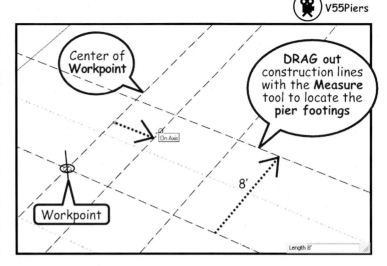

Center of **Workpoint**

DRAG out construction lines with the **Measure** tool to locate the pier footings

Workpoint

8'

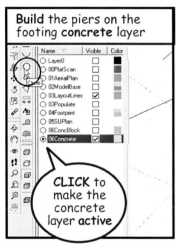

**Build** the piers on the footing **concrete** layer

CLICK to make the concrete layer **active**

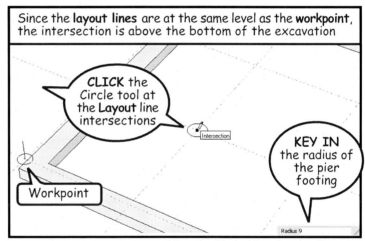

Since the **layout lines** are at the same level as the **workpoint**, the intersection is above the bottom of the excavation

CLICK the Circle tool at the **Layout** line intersections

KEY IN the radius of the pier footing

Workpoint

*See the 2D drawings for the dimensions

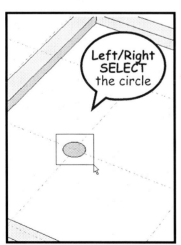

Left/Right SELECT the circle

RIGHT CLICK and Group

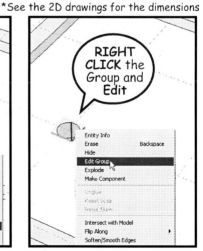

RIGHT CLICK the Group and Edit

# Pour the Pier Footing

Edit the **Circle** group like you did the concrete **block**, except **Push/Pull** downward

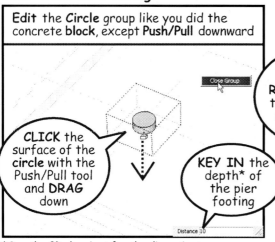

**CLICK** the surface of the **circle** with the Push/Pull tool and **DRAG** down

Close Group

**KEY IN** the depth* of the pier footing

Distance :10

*See the 2D drawings for the dimensions

**Components** can be edited **later** to change their **shape** or **size** from a **cylinder**

**Close** the group then **RIGHT CLICK** the Group and select **Make Component**

Entity Info
Erase                    Backspace
Hide
Edit Group
Explode
Make Component
Unglue
Reset Scale
Reset Skew
Intersect with Model
Flip Along

**CTRL CLICK** the cylinder **center** with the **Move** tool

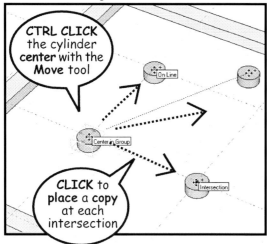

On Line
Center in Group
Intersection

**CLICK** to **place** a **copy** at each intersection

**SELECT** all 4 cylinders and then **CLICK** the top of the **stake with** the **Move** tool

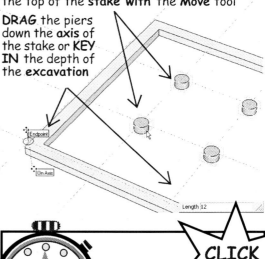

**DRAG** the piers down the **axis** of the stake or **KEY IN** the depth of the **excavation**

Endpoint
On Axis
Length :12

## DO YOU KNOW HOW TO:

1. Move around with the Camera tools
2. Use the workpoint to layout the footing
3. Drop a plumb-line for vertical reference
4. Use the Offset tool
5. Use Push/Pull to pour the footing
6. Make multiple copies with CTRL drag
7. Shift-Lock the plane of rotation
8. Use CTRL to make a rotation copy
9. Use inferences to assemble objects

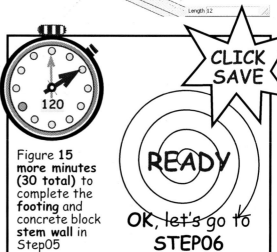

120

Figure **15** **more minutes (30 total)** to complete the **footing** and concrete block **stem wall** in Step05

**CLICK SAVE**

**READY**

OK, let's go to **STEP06**

56

# Step06: Floor Framing
## 3D CONSTRUCTION MODELING

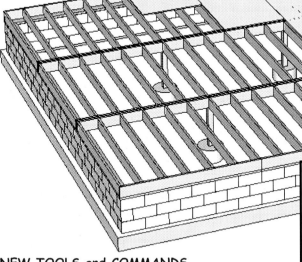

Budget about **45 minutes** for Step06.

**Be sure** to turn SketchUp off when thinking...or resting...or **anything.**

## NEW TOOLS and COMMANDS

Page views of the model

Hide
Unhide All
Unhide Last

**Pages**
Add | Update | Delete | ▶
ZoomOut
PierB1
SouthWest
LayDown
Girder
GirderOut

## WHAT YOU WILL DO

1. Hide/Unhide the building footprint
2. Set up a framing layer for the framing
3. Fabricate lumber from a block of wood

4. RIGHT CLICK to Edit Just This One component
6. Move and CTRL COPY the framing Components

7. Modify lumber lengths to match other walls

8. Add common views as Page tabs

9. Fabricate the subfloor and place on framing

## MORE NEW WORDS TO REVIEW

Blocking: framing placed between joist
Fabrication process: modeling sequence
Framing: assembly of pieces as a system
Girder: large supporting beam
Joists: floor or ceiling framing member
Nominal: the listed size, not actual size
Pier: short column for a concentrated load
Sheathing: surface material for framing
Sill: lowest member of the framing system
Page View: user saved views of the model
Pier: short column for a concentrated load
Post: vertical support in framing system
Stringline: a horizontal reference line
Subfloor: flooring laid on framing joists

*Though a framing manual is not necessary for Step06, you may want to use one as a reference

Reset the **layers** so you can **focus** on the framing...

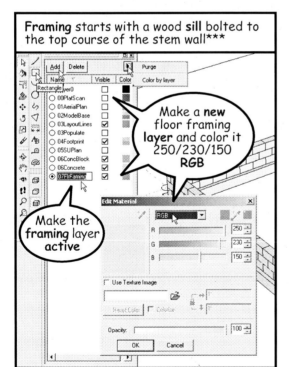

Make the footprint **layer\*** and massing model **visible**

Zoom Window

Undo View Change

With the **foundation** and massing model visible it's easier to **see** the shape and **scope** of the work.

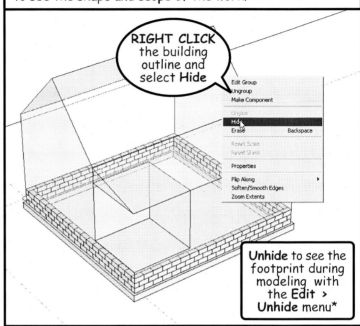

**RIGHT CLICK** the building outline and select **Hide**

Edit Group
Ungroup
Make Component
Unglue
Hide
Erase                    Backspace
Reset Scale
Reset Skew
Properties
Flip Along
Soften/Smooth Edges
Zoom Extents

**Unhide** to see the footprint during modeling with the **Edit > Unhide** menu\*

*See Unhide menu on page 65

**Framing** starts with a wood **sill** bolted to the top course of the stem wall\*\*\*

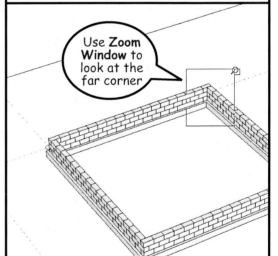

Make a **new** floor framing **layer** and color it 250/230/150 **RGB**

Make the **framing** layer active

Edit Material
RGB
R          250
G          230
B          150
☐ Use Texture Image
Reset Color  ☐ Colorize
Opacity:      100
OK      Cancel

Zoom out to view the overall scope then **zoom in** to focus on the work\*\*

Use **Zoom Window** to look at the far corner

\*\*Repeatedly reviewing scope (zooming out) while working on the details (zooming in) will come naturally as you become more proficient at navigating the model

\*\*\*See the 2D drawings

## Fabricate the Mud Sill

**Fabricating** lumber for the framing is similar to making the concrete block in Step05.

1. **DRAG** out a rectangle (the nominal width by **12" long**)

2. **Group** the rectangle and **RIGHT CLICK** for **editing**

3. **Pull up** the rectangle to the milled **thickness***

4. Pull out (**extrude**) the block to the length of the **lumber**

5 Close the group and make it a **component**

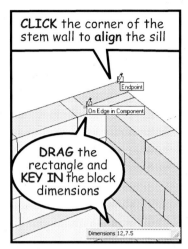

**CLICK** the corner of the stem wall to **align** the sill

Endpoint

On Edge in Component

**DRAG** the rectangle and **KEY IN** the block dimensions

Dimensions :12,7.5

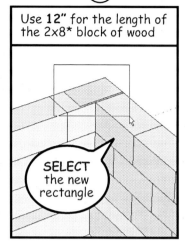

Use **12"** for the length of the **2x8*** block of wood

**SELECT** the new rectangle

A **3D block** is created from this **2D rectangle**

**RIGHT CLICK** and **Group**

Entity Info
Erase          Backspace
Hide

Select
Area
Make Component
Make Group        G
Intersect with Model
Reverse Faces

Edit the **2D** group to fabricate a **block** of wood

**RIGHT CLICK** and **Edit Group**

Entity Info
Erase          Backspace
Hide
Edit Group
Explode
Make Component

Intersect with Model

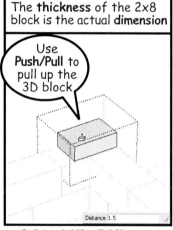

The **thickness** of the 2x8 block is the actual **dimension**

Use **Push/Pull** to pull up the 3D block

Distance :1.5

*The actual size of lumber is smaller than its listed nominal size. For example, a 2x8 is < 1-1/2 x 7-1/2

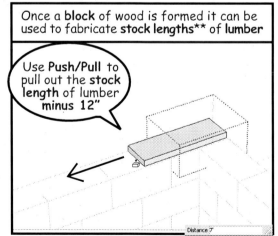

Once a **block** of wood is formed it can be used to fabricate **stock lengths**** of **lumber**

Use **Push/Pull** to pull out the **stock length** of lumber **minus 12"**

Distance :7

The **block** can also be **saved** and stored to make different stock lengths **later*****

**RIGHT CLICK** and **Close Group**

Close Group

Then **RIGHT CLICK** the group and **Make Component**

**Stock length of lumber is normally 8', 10', and 12' minus the original 12" length of the wood block

***To save the block, close the group and use Move and CTRL key to place a copy in the lay down area

**V58SillPlate**

Use **Zoom Window** and **Undo Zoom Change** tools

First **CLICK** to select* the **sill**

Then **CLICK** the **Move** tool

**CLICK SAVE**

**Copies** of the framing **components** can be **duplicated** in the **same way** as making copies of **concrete block** in Step05

**HOLD** the **CTRL** key down and **CLICK** the corner*

Then **CLICK** to **place** the **copy** at the other end*

Repeat the **CTRL CLICK** and place another **copy**

*The point of selection is the point of placement

You can rotate **copies** around the corner in the same way as **rotating** copies of the concrete blocks in **Step05**

**SELECT** the sill, then **CLICK** the **Rotate** tool**

Press the **Shift Key** to **lock** the rotation plane to the **horizontal**

**CLICK** to set the **center** of **rotation**

Then **CTRL CLICK** the edge of the component to set the **axis** of the rotation

Use **Inferences** and Zoom tools to **place** the sill

**Rotate** the sill around the axis and **CLICK** to place the copy on the **wall**

**KEY IN** the angle

**The Move and Rotate tool requires you to select the object to move or rotate first

## Trim the stock lengths

Absolute **accuracy** is not necessary but it's good to **zoom** in **to check alignment**- - just in case

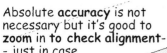

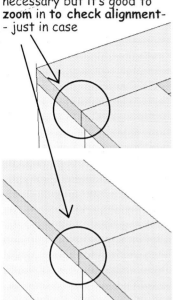

To trim stock material

To trim stock material

RIGHT CLICK and Edit Just This One

Use **Push Pull** to adjust length to fit

RIGHT CLICK and Close

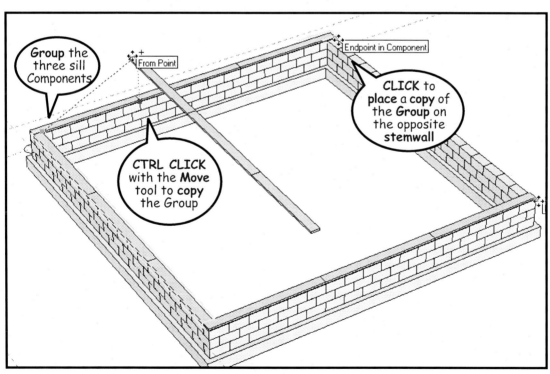

Group the three sill Components

CTRL CLICK with the **Move** tool to **copy** the Group

CLICK to **place** a **copy** of the **Group** on the opposite **stemwall**

61

# Object Fabrication Process

CLICK SAVE

Figure
**10 minutes**
to complete
this portion of
the floor framing

130

Fabricating pieces for any part of the construction is the same process for concrete blocks, pier footings, or lumber:

1. Use a tool like the rectangle or circle to draw a 2D shape

2. DRAG a Left/Right box around the shape to select it

3. RIGHT CLICK the selection and Group it

4. RIGHT CLICK the Group and choose Edit Group

5. Push/Pull to extrude the shape into a 3D object

6. RIGHT CLICK and close the Group when finished editing

7. RIGHT CLICK the Group and make it a Component if it is likely to change later or you plan to make a lot of copies

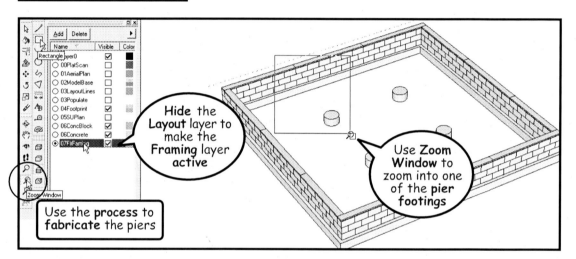

**Hide** the **Layout** layer to make the **Framing** layer active

Use **Zoom Window** to zoom into one of the **pier footings**

Use the **process** to **fabricate** the piers

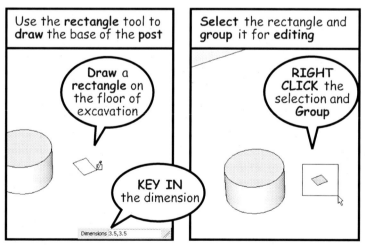

Use the **rectangle** tool to **draw** the base of the **post**

Draw a **rectangle** on the floor of excavation

**KEY IN** the dimension

Dimensions 3.5,3.5

**Select** the rectangle and **group** it for **editing**

**RIGHT CLICK** the selection and **Group**

**Move** a **corner** of the group to the **center** of the **pier**

**Select** the Group and use the **Move** tool to place the **rectangle**

On Face in Component

# Fabricate a Post for the Piers

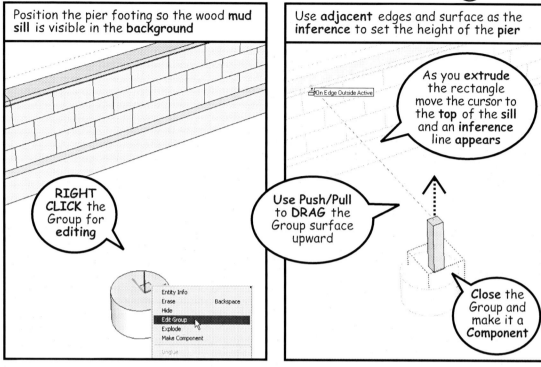

Position the pier footing so the wood **mud sill** is visible in the **background**

> **RIGHT CLICK** the Group for **editing**

| Entity Info | |
|---|---|
| Erase | Backspace |
| Hide | |
| Edit Group | |
| Explode | |
| Make Component | |

Use **adjacent** edges and surface as the **inference** to set the height of the **pier**

On Edge Outside Active

> As you **extrude** the rectangle move the cursor to the **top** of the **sill** and an **inference** line **appears**

> Use Push/Pull to **DRAG** the Group surface upward

> **Close** the Group and make it a **Component**

---

The **post** now extends from the **top** of the **pier** to the **top** of the **sill** (or **underside** of the **girder**)

**Next** it's a matter of centering the post on the pier footing:

Use inferences with the Move tool to **align** the geometry of the two objects:

1. **Center** of the pier

2. **Midpoint** of the post

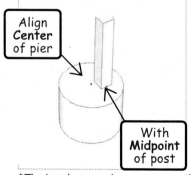

Align **Center** of pier

With **Midpoint** of post

> **SELECT** the post

> **CLICK** the **Move** tool at the **Midpoint** of the post

> **CLICK** the inference center of the footing to **place**

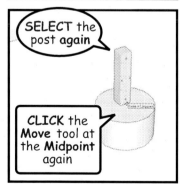

> **SELECT** the post **again**

> **CLICK** the **Move** tool at the **Midpoint** again

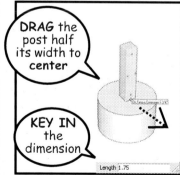

> **DRAG** the post half its width to **center**

> **KEY IN** the dimension

Length 1.75

*The brackets, anchors, straps, nails, screws, and nuts and bolts can be added later - if you like

63

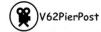

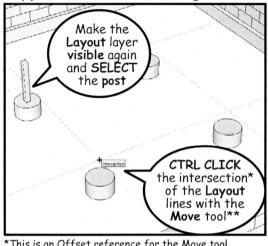

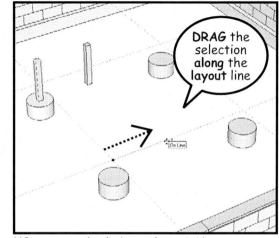

*This is an Offset reference for the Move tool

**Be sure to make the Layout layer visible

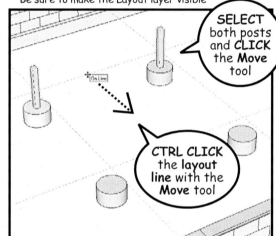

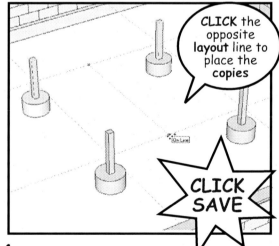

# Page Views

 V65PageVu

Preset **Page views** make **moving** around the model a lot faster and **easier**. Page views can be added, deleted, and updated

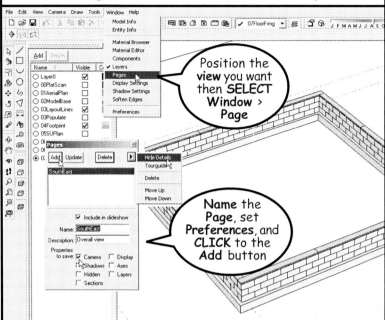

Position the view you want then **SELECT** Window > Page

Name the **Page**, set **Preferences**, and **CLICK** to the Add button

*Preferences set the options you want to keep with the view

**Add a Page** any time you think you might be **returning** to a particular **view**.

Set **Preferences\*** to **maximize** flexibility from view to view or to keep Layer or Hide preferences for that particular view.

**For example**, check the Camera preference and **uncheck all** other Preferences and **only** the point of **view** will be **saved** for that view. This is good for **quickly moving** around without changing the model

Selecting the Layer, Hidden, or any other preference will **save** those **settings** with the Page view

Page preferences can be **changed** individually or as a group **later**

---

**UnHide** the massing model to visualize the **scope**

**SELECT** Edit and **Unhide All** to see the footprint

**Visibility** of the transparent **massing model** for the building can be **controlled** with the **Visible button** or Hide/Unhide\*\*

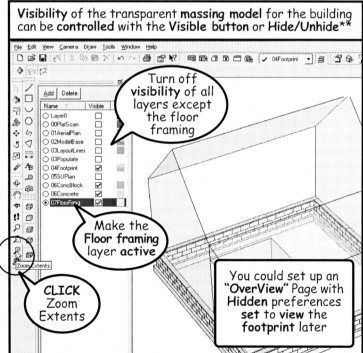

Turn off **visibility** of all layers except the floor framing

Make the **Floor framing** layer **active**

**CLICK** Zoom Extents

You could set up an **"OverView"** Page with **Hidden** preferences **set** to **view** the **footprint** later

65 \*\*RIGHT CLICK any object and SELECT Hide, you can Unhide Last or Unhide All with the Edit Menu

# Set up the Laydown Area

As you change views, **RIGHT CLICK** to **Add** new pages or **Update** current changes*

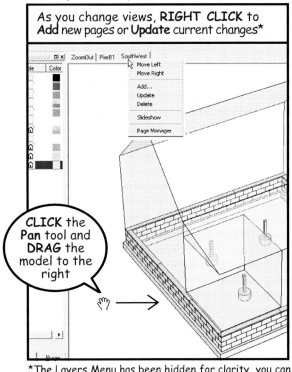

CLICK the **Pan** tool and **DRAG** the model to the right

The **floor girder** can be fabricated in place or off to the side and **moved** in later

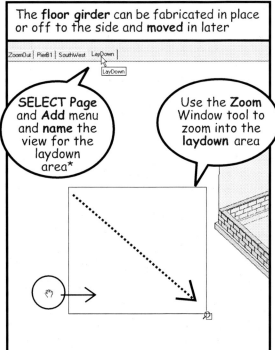

SELECT Page and **Add** menu and **name** the view for the laydown area*

Use the **Zoom** Window tool to zoom into the **laydown** area

*The Layers Menu has been hidden for clarity, you can leave yours on

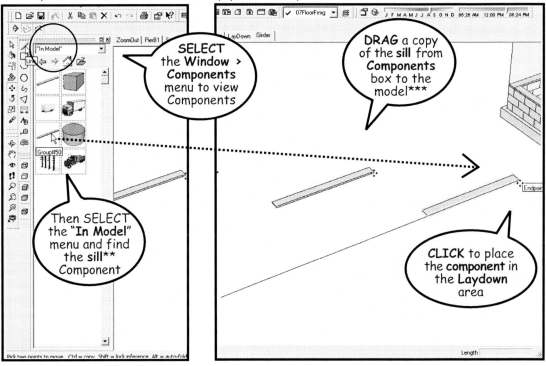

SELECT the **Window > Components** menu to view Components

Then SELECT the "**In Model**" menu and find the **sill**** Component

DRAG a copy of the **sill** from **Components** box to the model***

CLICK to place the **component** in the **Laydown** area

**Make sure you have the 8 foot piece and not a "trimmed" version

66

***Notice that the Move tool is automatically active as you DRAG

# Build a Composite Girder

**Measure** the length of the component to **make sure** it is the **stock 8' length***

CLICK the **Measure** tool on both ends of the sill

Length 8'

CTRL CLICK the Component with the **Move** tool

Endpoint

Endpoint in Component

Repeat to **place** 2 copies end to end

*You can also Right Click the Component and name it in Properties

Continue to **CTRL CLICK** Components with the **Move** tool

Midpoint in Component

Endpoint in Component

**Place** one copy at each **Midpoint**

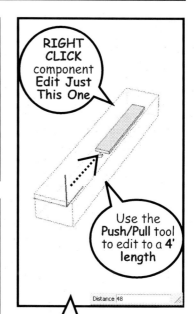

**RIGHT CLICK** component **Edit Just This One**

Use the **Push/Pull** tool to edit to a **4'** length

Distance 48

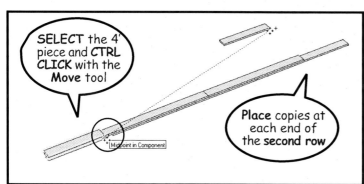

**SELECT** the 4' piece and **CTRL CLICK** with the **Move** tool

Midpoint in Component

**Place** copies at each end of the **second row**

**SELECT** the 3 pieces on the **bottom** of the **stack**

Then **CTRL CLICK** with **Move** and copy them to the **top** row

⭐ CLICK SAVE

140

Figure **10 minutes** to complete this portion of the **floor framing**

67

## Place the Girder on the Foundation

SELECT the three rows of lumber and **Group** as a single composite girder

Use the **Orbit** and **Zoom** tools to view the end of the **Group**

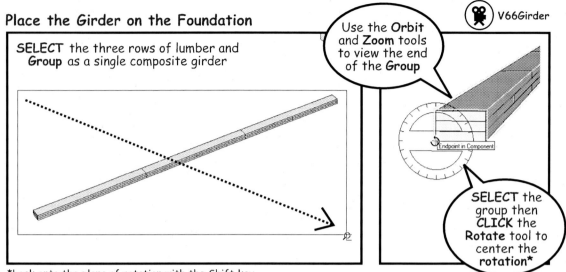

Endpoint in Component

SELECT the group then CLICK the **Rotate** tool to center the **rotation***

*Lock onto the plane of rotation with the Shift key

CLICK the edge to set the **axis** of rotation

KEY IN the angle

Angle : 90.0

**Zoom in** to the end of the group and use the **Line** tool to mark a vertical **centerline** from midpoint to midpoint

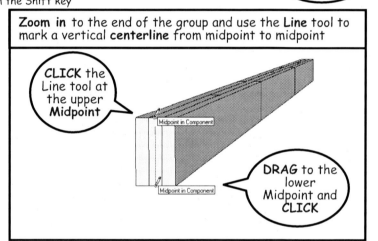

CLICK the Line tool at the upper **Midpoint**

Midpoint in Component

DRAG to the lower Midpoint and CLICK

Midpoint in Component

SELECT both the **line** and the **girder**

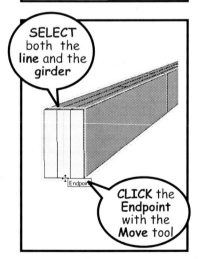

Endpoint

CLICK the Endpoint with the **Move** tool

With the **Move** tool still **active** use the **Camera** tools and **Pages** to position the **view** of the girder for **placement**

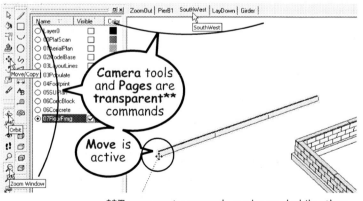

ZoomOut  PierB1  SouthWest  LayDown  Girder

SouthWest

| Name | Visible | Color |
| --- | --- | --- |
| Layer0 | | |
| 00PlatScan | | |
| 01AerialPlan | | |
| 02ModelBase | | |
| 03LayoutLines | | |
| 03Populate | | |
| 04Footprint | | |
| 05SUPlat | | |
| 06ConcBlock | | |
| 06Concrete | | |
| 07FloorFrmg | ✓ | |

Move/Copy

Orbit

Zoom Window

Camera tools and **Pages** are **transparent****
commands

Move is active

68

**Transparent commands can be used while other commands are still active, RIGHT CLICK to Exit.

# Place the Girder in Position

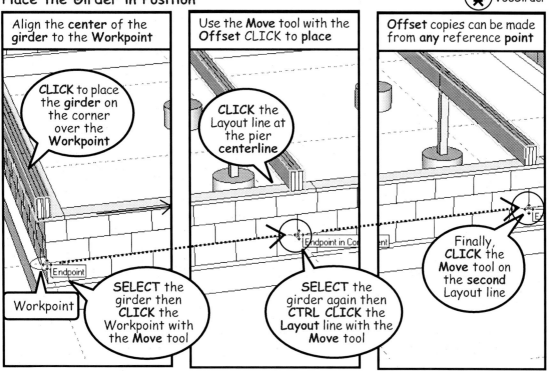

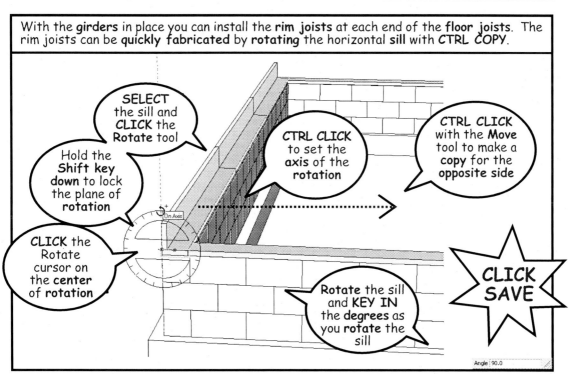

# Place the Floor Joists

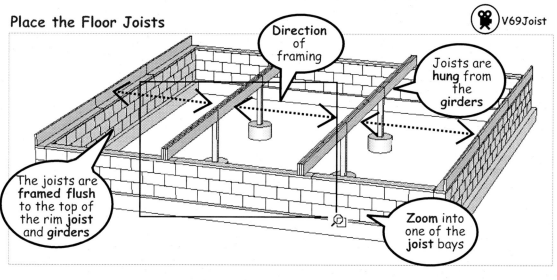

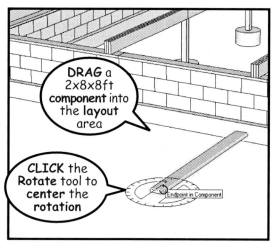

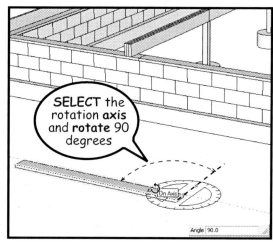

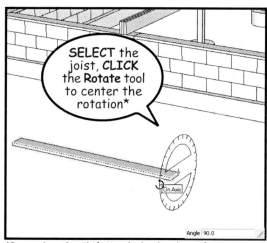

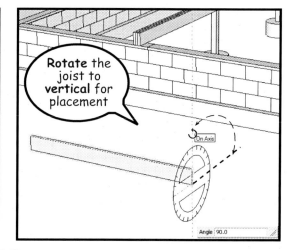

*Remember the Shift Key locks the plane of rotation on any horizontal or vertical surface

70

# Place the Floor Joists

V69Joist

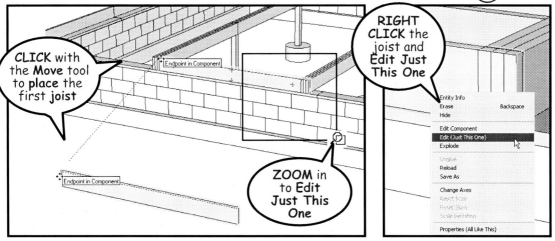

CLICK with the **Move** tool to **place the first joist**

RIGHT CLICK the joist and **Edit Just This One**

ZOOM in to **Edit Just This One**

Endpoint in Component

Endpoint in Component

Entity Info
Erase                          Backspace
Hide

Edit Component
Edit (Just This One)
Explode

Unglue
Reload
Save As

Change Axes
Reset Scale
Reset Skew
Scale Definition

Properties (All Like This)

**Create** multiple copies of the **new joist** Component perpendicular to the **edge** of the girder (the **Red Axis**)

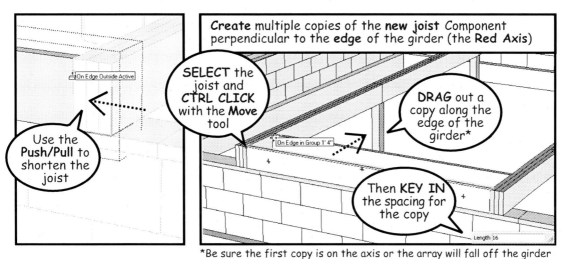

Use the **Push/Pull** to shorten the joist

On Edge Outside Active

SELECT the joist and **CTRL CLICK** with the **Move** tool

On Edge in Group 1' 4"

DRAG out a copy along the edge of the girder*

Then **KEY IN** the spacing for the copy

Length :16

*Be sure the first copy is on the axis or the array will fall off the girder

Immediately **KEY IN** the **number of copies** followed by an X**

Length :18x

Follow the same process*** for the floor **joists** in the **other bays.**

1. **Position** the first joist and Edit the length with **Edit Just This One** to fit each bay

2. **Select** the joists, then CTRL CLICK with **Move**

3. **DRAG** out a single copy, **KEY IN** the spacing, then

4. Immediately **KEY IN** the **number of copies** followed by an **X**

**Remember SketchUp is waiting for KEY IN value, a CLICK will cancel the command. Just press the Escape Key and UNDO if a problem

***This is the same as the object fabrication process on Page 62

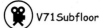
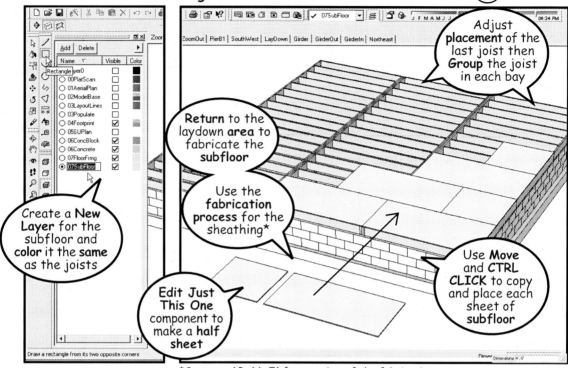

Adjust **placement** of the last joist then **Group** the joist in each bay

**Return** to the laydown **area** to fabricate the **subfloor**

Use the **fabrication process** for the sheathing*

Create a **New Layer** for the subfloor and **color** it the **same** as the joists

**Edit Just This One** component to make a **half sheet**

Use **Move** and **CTRL CLICK** to copy and place each sheet of **subfloor**

*See page 62, 66, 71 for a review of the fabrication process

---

**CLICK SAVE**

**45 minutes** max for Step06.

You are getting faster...right?

**165**

**SAVE YOUR MINUTES**

(Remember to close the program when not in use)

**READY**

OK, let's go to **STEP07**

## DO YOU KNOW HOW TO:

1. Use camera tools to view the model from any angle
2. Set up and name layers, colors, and set visibility
3. Change layer visibility and Hide/Unhide objects
4. Insert a component and Edit Just This One
5. Fabricate objects like joists, piers, and subfloor
6. Make copies with the Move tool and Ctrl key
7. Make multiple copies with Move and CTRL CLICK
8. Rotate and copy with the CTRL CLICK
9. Use inferences to place objects in an assembly
10. Use offset references to move and copy
11. Add Pages for preset views of the model

# Step07: Wall Framing
## BASIC 3D CONSTRUCTION MODELING

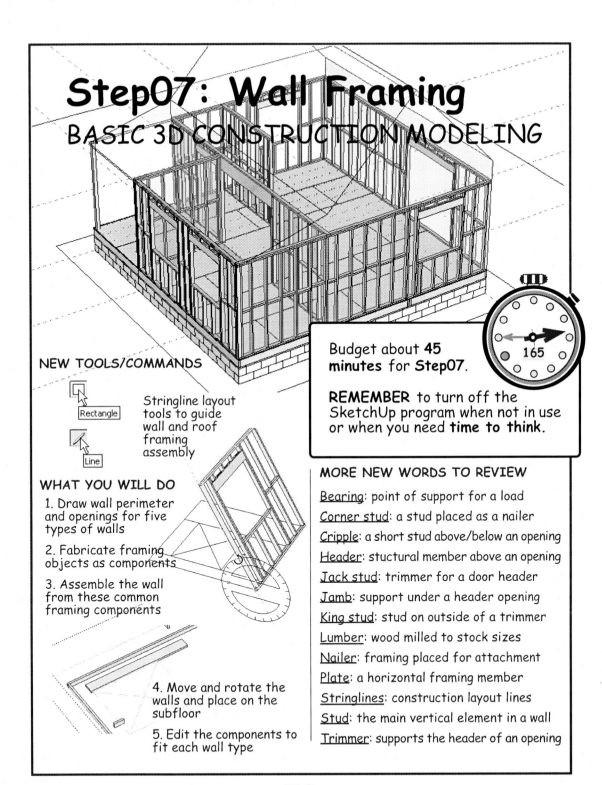

Budget about **45 minutes** for **Step07**.

**REMEMBER** to turn off the SketchUp program when not in use or when you need **time to think.**

## NEW TOOLS/COMMANDS

Rectangle

Line

Stringline layout tools to guide wall and roof framing assembly

## WHAT YOU WILL DO

1. Draw wall perimeter and openings for five types of walls

2. Fabricate framing objects as components

3. Assemble the wall from these common framing components

4. Move and rotate the walls and place on the subfloor

5. Edit the components to fit each wall type

## MORE NEW WORDS TO REVIEW

<u>Bearing</u>: point of support for a load

<u>Corner stud</u>: a stud placed as a nailer

<u>Cripple</u>: a short stud above/below an opening

<u>Header</u>: stuctural member above an opening

<u>Jack stud</u>: trimmer for a door header

<u>Jamb</u>: support under a header opening

<u>King stud</u>: stud on outside of a trimmer

<u>Lumber</u>: wood milled to stock sizes

<u>Nailer</u>: framing placed for attachment

<u>Plate</u>: a horizontal framing member

<u>Stringlines</u>: construction layout lines

<u>Stud</u>: the main vertical element in a wall

<u>Trimmer</u>: supports the header of an opening

# Layout Framing for Wall01

You can now **backfill** the **excavation** by rotating the **fill** and **moving** it into place*

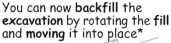

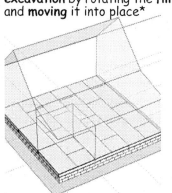

**Shift Lock** the plane of **rotation** onto the side of the stem wall

*Backfill is completed after floor framing in actual construction

---

Make a **new layer** active for the **wall** framing using the same color as the other **framing** materials

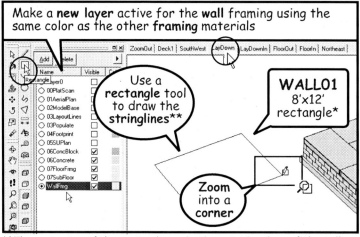

Use a **rectangle** tool to draw the **stringlines****

**WALL01** 8'x12' rectangle*

Zoom into a corner

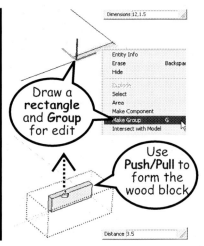

Draw a **rectangle** and **Group** for edit

Use **Push/Pull** to form the wood block

**The perimeter of the rectangle marks the outside edges of the wall

---

Use the **Push/Pull** tool to extrude the wood block as a **stock length** of **lumber**

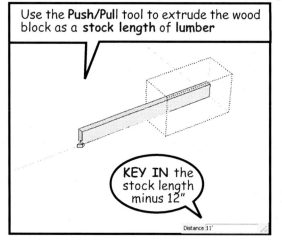

**KEY IN** the stock length minus 12"

Close the **Group** and make it a **component**. It'll be used as plates for the **framing*****

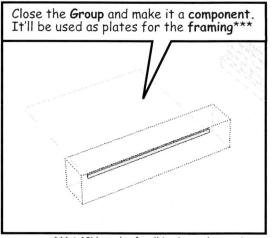

***A 12' length of wall is about the maximum a crew can lift and handle safely

CTRL CLICK with the **Move** tool to copy the **plate** to the top*

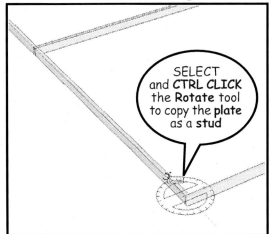

SELECT and **CTRL CLICK** the **Rotate** tool to copy the **plate** as a **stud**

*A second top plate is added when all walls are in place

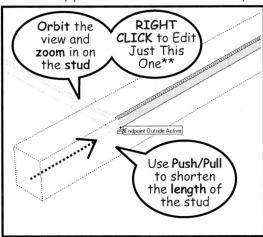

Orbit the view and **zoom** in on the **stud**

**RIGHT CLICK** to Edit Just This One**

Use **Push/Pull** to shorten the **length** of the stud

**Edit Just One creates a new component

CTRL CLICK the **Move** tool to copy a **corner stud**

KEY IN the distance

The **corner stud** acts as a **nailer** for interior finishes

Length 3

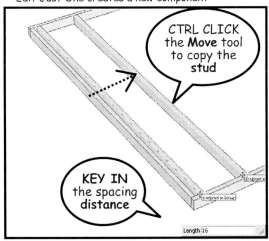

CTRL CLICK the **Move** tool to copy the **stud**

KEY IN the spacing distance

Length :16

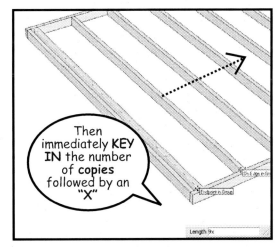

Then immediately **KEY IN** the number of **copies** followed by an "X"

Length 9x

75

# Setting Studs for Wall01

V73Wall01

Use **Camera** tools to **check** your assembly and the fit

Use the **Move** tool to **adjust** placement of the **last stud**

Endpoint in Group

**Copy** and **modify** the plate for **other** framing **members**

CTRL CLICK the **Move** tool to **copy** the plate for editing

Endpoint in Group

**Edit** the plate lengths to fit studs as **blocking**

RIGHT CLICK and Edit Just This One*

Use the **Push/Pull** tool to **fit studs**

*Edit Just This One creates a new component

**Rotate** blocking and **place** between the **corner studs**

Midpoint in Group

Insert a **block** at the **corner** stud as a **nailer**

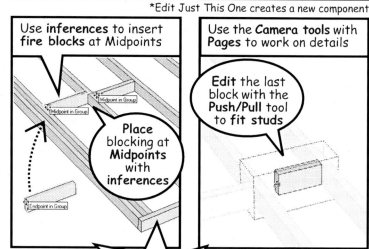

Use **inferences** to insert **fire blocks** at Midpoints

Midpoint in Group
Midpoint in Group

**Place** blocking at **Midpoints** with inferences

Endpoint in Group

Use the **Camera tools** with **Pages** to work on details

**Edit** the last block with the **Push/Pull** tool to **fit studs**

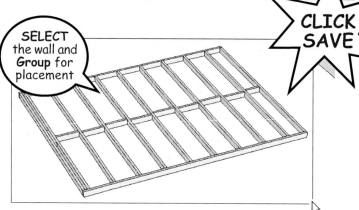

SELECT the wall and **Group** for placement

CLICK SAVE

**Framing** the **Wall01** gives you an idea of how to do the **other walls**. The process:

1. Draw the stringlines
2. Lay down the plates
3. Set the end/corner studs
4. Fill in the wall studs
5. Insert blocking

Figure about **10 minutes** to frame your first wall.

175

The resulting wall is a **group** of reusable **framing** Components that can be **copied and pasted** into the other wall **types**

76

# Layout Framing for Wall02

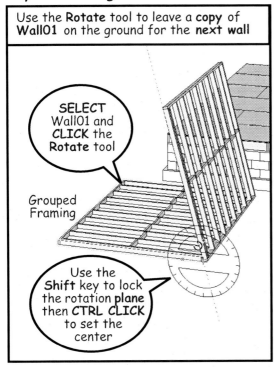

Use the **Rotate** tool to leave a **copy** of **Wall01** on the ground for the **next wall**

SELECT Wall01 and **CLICK** the **Rotate** tool

Grouped Framing

Use the **Shift** key to lock the rotation **plane** then **CTRL CLICK** to set the center

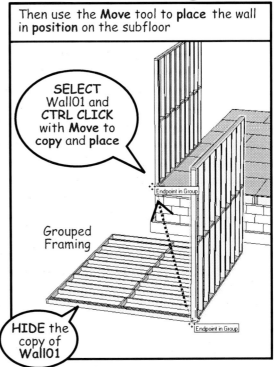

Then use the **Move** tool to **place** the wall in **position** on the subfloor

SELECT Wall01 and **CTRL CLICK** with **Move** to **copy** and **place**

Endpoint in Group

Grouped Framing

**HIDE** the copy of **Wall01**

Endpoint in Group

## WALL02

Use the **rectangle** and **line** tools with the **Move** tool and the **CTRL** key to move and copy and modify the **stringlines** for **Wall02**. Snap the framing components to the stringlines*

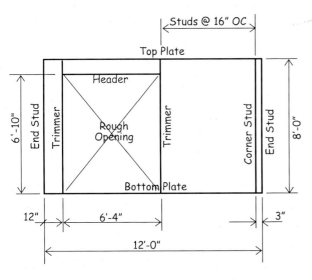

Studs @ 16" OC

Top Plate

Header

End Stud

Trimmer

Rough Opening

Trimmer

Corner Stud

End Stud

Bottom Plate

6'-10"

8'-0"

12"    6'-4"    3"

12'-0"

Group the **stringlines before** placing the wall or the lines will **attach** to the **framing** members

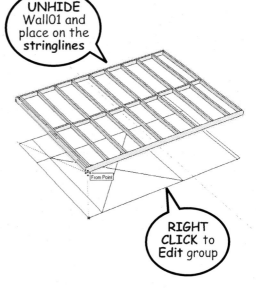

UNHIDE Wall01 and place on the **stringlines**

From Point

RIGHT CLICK to Edit group

*Wall layouts are the responsibility of the contractor and are done in the field

77

## Framing Wall02

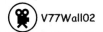

**Right Click** and edit the grouped components for Wall01. **Delete** studs that are no longer necessary and use grouped **stringlines** to guide the new Wall02 assembly. Remember the **Camera** tools and **Pages** make moving around and editing alot easier.*

Use (your well practiced) **editing skills** to **Right Click** the existing components and adjust lengths for trimmers and cripples in the new wall.

Use the **fabrication** process to make a **header** from a **block** of wood**

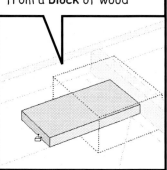

**As a group rather than a component

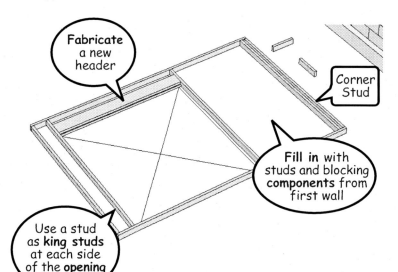

Fabricate a new header

Corner Stud

Fill **in** with studs and blocking **components** from first wall

Use a stud as **king studs** at each side of the **opening**

**Edit Just This One** stud component to fit as a **cripple** over the **header**

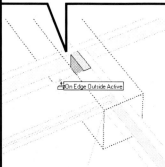

On Edge Outside Active

**Jack** studs or **trimmers** go inside the **king studs** to support the header

**Edit Just This One** stud to make the **trimmer**

**CTRL CLICK** with the **Move** tool to make **single** or **multiple** copies of the **cripples** and studs

*Camera and Page tools are transparent and can be used in the middle of other commands

78

## Layout the Framing for Wall03

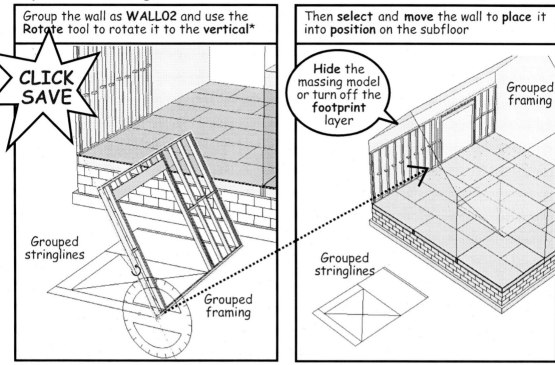

Group the wall as **WALL02** and use the **Rotate** tool to rotate it to the **vertical***

CLICK SAVE

Grouped stringlines

Grouped framing

Then **select** and **move** the wall to **place** it into **position** on the subfloor

**Hide** the massing model or turn off the **footprint** layer

Grouped framing

Grouped stringlines

*You can rotate and copy the wall back later to use as a template

## WALL03

Draw the **stringlines** for the Wall03 using the rectangle and line tools. Snap the components to the **grouped** layout lines in the same way as Wall01 and Wall02.

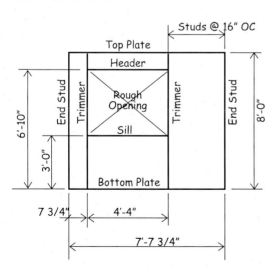

Studs @ 16" OC

Top Plate

Header

End Stud

Trimmer

Rough Opening

Trimmer

End Stud

Sill

8'-0"

6'-10"

3'-0"

Bottom Plate

7 3/4"     4'-4"

7'-7 3/4"

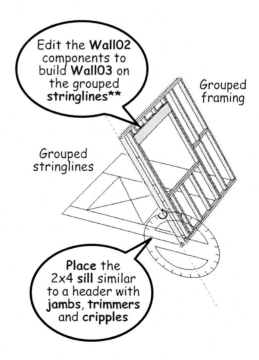

Edit the **Wall02** components to build **Wall03** on the grouped **stringlines****

Grouped framing

Grouped stringlines

**Place** the 2x4 **sill** similar to a header with **jambs, trimmers** and **cripples**

79

**Use Edit Just This One. When you edit a component, every component copy changes.

# Frame Wall03

Wall03 is an edited version of the Wall02 components

1. Draw the stringlines
2. Lay down the plates
3. Set the end/corner studs
4. Place king studs
5. Insert headers and sill
6. Place cripples
7. Fill in with studs and blocking

Budget **5** minutes for **each wall** when you reuse wall components

180

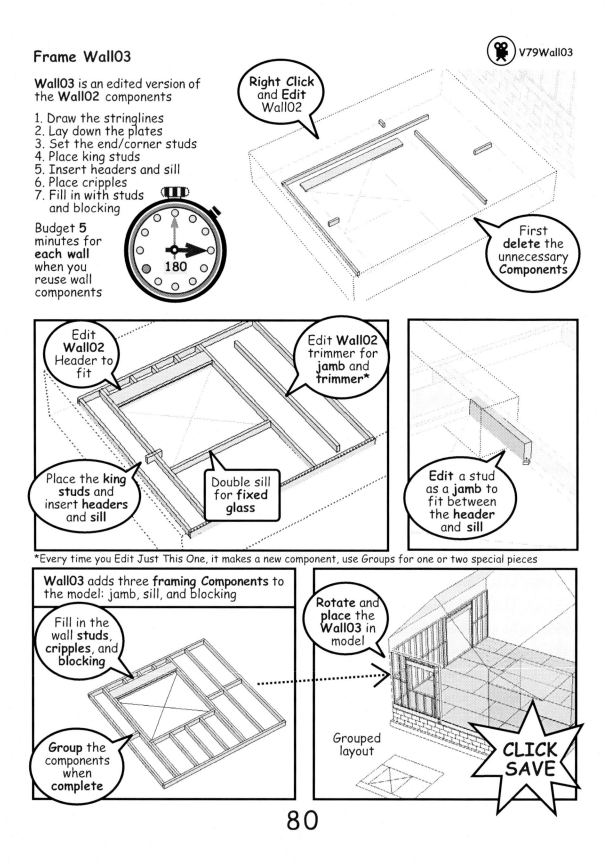

Right Click and Edit Wall02

First **delete** the unnecessary Components

Edit **Wall02** Header to fit

Edit **Wall02** trimmer for **jamb** and **trimmer***

Place the **king studs** and insert **headers** and **sill**

Double sill for **fixed glass**

**Edit** a stud as a **jamb** to fit between the **header** and **sill**

*Every time you Edit Just This One, it makes a new component, use Groups for one or two special pieces

**Wall03** adds three **framing Components** to the model: jamb, sill, and blocking

Fill in the wall **studs, cripples,** and **blocking**

**Group** the components when **complete**

Rotate and **place** the **Wall03** in model

Grouped layout

CLICK SAVE

80

# Layout the Framing for Wall04

 V81Wall04

## WALL04

**Modify** existing components from **Wall01**

Add **corner studs** as nailers at adjoining partitions

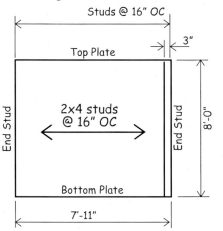

Studs @ 16" OC

Top Plate

3"

End Stud

2x4 studs @ 16" OC

End Stud

8'-0"

Bottom Plate

7'-11"

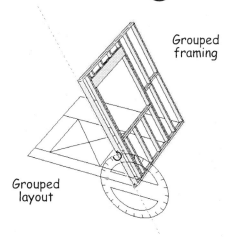

Grouped framing

Grouped layout

---

**Wall04** is an edited version of **Wall01** with **corner** studs as required at **partitions**

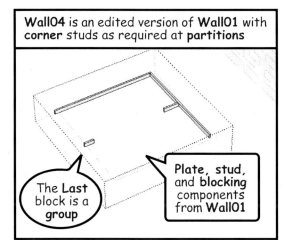

The **Last** block is a **group**

**Plate, stud,** and **blocking** components from Wall01

---

SELECT the stud and blocking and **CTRL CLICK** with the **Move** tool*

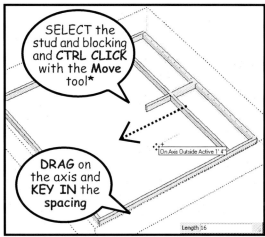

On Axis Outside Active 1' 4"

DRAG on the axis and **KEY IN** the spacing

Length 16

*SELECT the objects and CLICK the Move tool outside the components

---

KEY IN the number of **copies** plus "X" then **delete** the extras

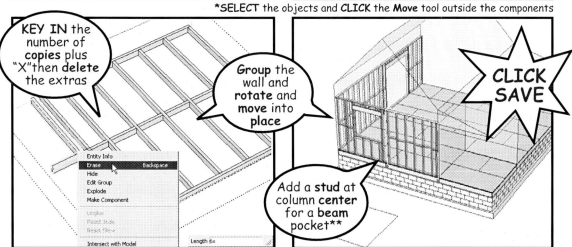

**Group** the wall and **rotate** and **move** into **place**

Entity Info
Erase          Backspace
Hide
Edit Group
Explode
Make Component

Unglue
Reset Scale
Reset Skew

Intersect with Model

Length 6x

Add a **stud** at column **center** for a **beam** pocket**

CLICK SAVE

**See 2D drawings for bearing condition

81

# Layout the Framing for Wall05

V82Wall05

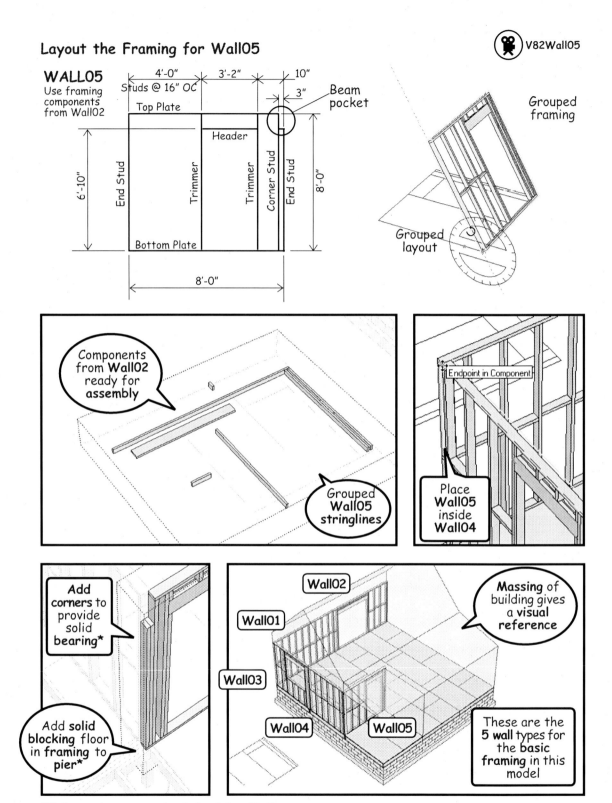

## WALL05
Use framing components from Wall02

4'-0"    3'-2"    10"
Studs @ 16" OC
3"
Beam pocket

Top Plate

Header

End Stud

Trimmer

Trimmer

Corner Stud

End Stud

6'-10"

8'-0"

Bottom Plate

8'-0"

Grouped framing

Grouped layout

Components from **Wall02** ready for **assembly**

Grouped **Wall05** stringlines

Endpoint in Component

Place **Wall05** inside **Wall04**

Add **corners** to provide solid bearing*

Add **solid blocking** floor in **framing** to pier*

Wall02

Wall01

Wall03

Wall04

Wall05

**Massing** of building gives a **visual reference**

These are the **5 wall** types for the **basic framing** in this model

*Nailers and corners are located and placed in the framing by the contractor in the field

82

# Complete the Wall Framing

Use this diagram to **rotate move** and **CTRL copy** these **same** five **walls** and complete the framing. Add **corner** studs and **partition nailers** to Wall types at the wall **intersections**.

Wall framing for **Wall02, 03, 04,** and **05** shouldn't take much more than **15 minutes**. That's about **30 minutes** to this point in Step07

Take **15 or so more minutes** to copy and **place walls** and edit corners and plates to **complete** the framing.

HIDE the **massing model** to place walls

Wall03

Wall02

Add a stud at **column center***

Wall04

Wall04

Wall01

Wall04

Wall04

Wall03

Wall05

Wall04

Wall04

Wall03

Wall03

Post*

CLICK SAVE

*Two interior columns not shown for clarity, see roof framing

Add **corner studs** to provide solid **bearing** at end of **Wall03****

See **2D drawings** for details on placement

Draw **stringlines** from the wall **plates**

On Edge Outside Active

Fabricate a **post** to **height** of adjacent **framing*****

**Make similar modifications at wall intersections

83

***Set posts on girder or sill for full bearing

*See 2D drawings for bearing condition

**Sheathing** would be added **after** the top **plates.** Wall sheathing is **not shown** in this model

Check your time. Say about **45 minutes** for Step07.

But you're **getting faster...** right?

**CLICK SAVE**

210

DO YOU KNOW HOW TO:

1. Draw stringlines with the line and rectangle tools
2. Fabricate a wood block as a framing component
3. Use components to assemble the Plates and Studs
3. Edit Just This One for blocking, sills, and plates
4. Frame the openings with jacks, trimmers, and cripples
5. Complete the framing with multiple copies
6. Rotate, copy, and place the walls onto the subfloor
7. Reuse the five walls to complete the framing
8. Modify the walls for beam pockets and intersections
9. Add posts and solid blocking to the wall frame
10. Add top plates to tie the framing together

**SAVE YOUR MINUTES**

**READY**

OK, let's go to **STEP08**

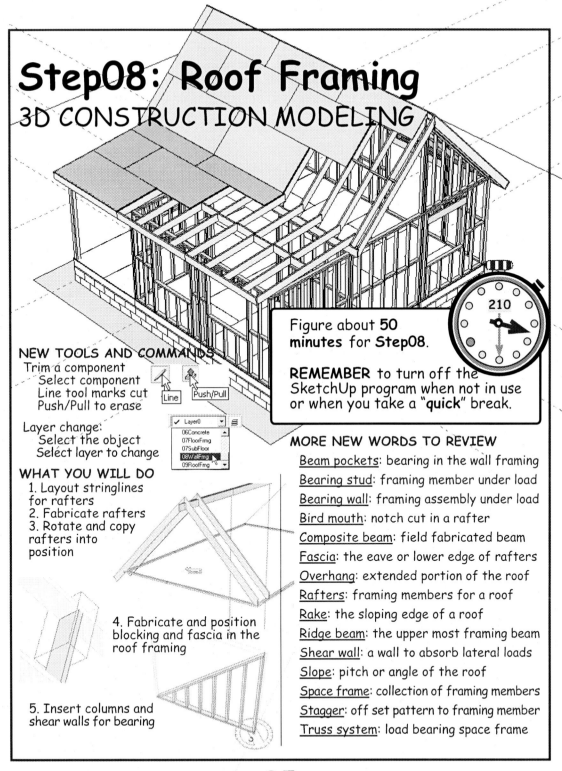

# Step08: Roof Framing
## 3D CONSTRUCTION MODELING

**NEW TOOLS AND COMMANDS**

Trim a component
  Select component
  Line tool marks cut
  Push/Pull to erase

Layer change:
  Select the object
  Select layer to change

Line

Push/Pull

✓ Layer0
06Concrete
07FloorFrmg
07SubFloor
08WallFrmg
09RoofFrmg

Figure about **50 minutes** for **Step08**.

**REMEMBER** to turn off the SketchUp program when not in use or when you take a "**quick**" break.

210

**WHAT YOU WILL DO**

1. Layout stringlines for rafters
2. Fabricate rafters
3. Rotate and copy rafters into position

4. Fabricate and position blocking and fascia in the roof framing

5. Insert columns and shear walls for bearing

**MORE NEW WORDS TO REVIEW**

<u>Beam pockets</u>: bearing in the wall framing
<u>Bearing stud</u>: framing member under load
<u>Bearing wall</u>: framing assembly under load
<u>Bird mouth</u>: notch cut in a rafter
<u>Composite beam</u>: field fabricated beam
<u>Fascia</u>: the eave or lower edge of rafters
<u>Overhang</u>: extended portion of the roof
<u>Rafters</u>: framing members for a roof
<u>Rake</u>: the sloping edge of a roof
<u>Ridge beam</u>: the upper most framing beam
<u>Shear wall</u>: a wall to absorb lateral loads
<u>Slope</u>: pitch or angle of the roof
<u>Space frame</u>: collection of framing members
<u>Stagger</u>: off set pattern to framing member
<u>Truss system</u>: load bearing space frame

# Roof Loading Diagram

The **roof framing** includes a **ridge beam** with **rafters** and **headers** at openings*

Note that a **truss system** could be substituted using almost the **same process** (but that's too easy).

The process:

1. Use **stringlines** to layout the framing stringlines in 2D

2. **Fabricate** the framing members as **components**

3. **Move** and **Rotate** the components with the **CTRL** key to **copy** and place the rafters

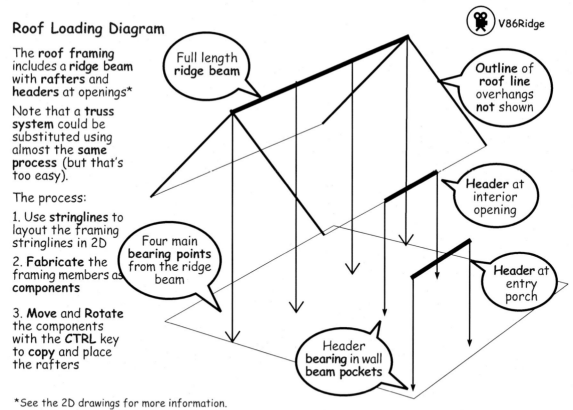

*See the 2D drawings for more information.

---

Adjust layer **visibility** for the roof **framing**

Use a copy of the floor **girder** as the ridge beam. After the copy, **change** the layer to the **new ridge layer**

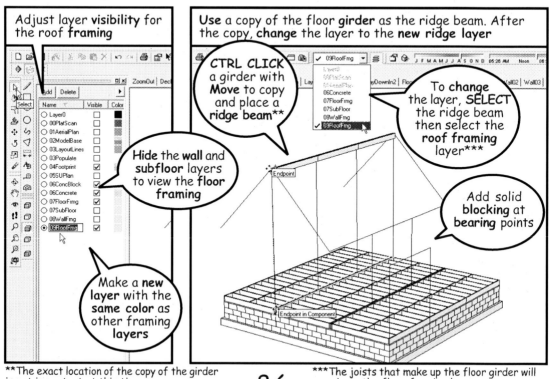

**CTRL CLICK** a girder with **Move** to copy and place a ridge beam**

To change the layer, SELECT the ridge beam then select the **roof framing** layer***

Hide the **wall** and **subfloor** layers to view the **floor framing**

Add solid **blocking** at **bearing** points

Make a **new layer** with the **same color** as other framing **layers**

---

**Full length ridge beam**

**Outline** of **roof line** overhangs **not** shown

**Header** at interior opening

**Four main bearing points** from the ridge beam

**Header** at entry porch

Header **bearing in wall beam pockets**

---

**The exact location of the copy of the girder is not important at this time

***The joists that make up the floor girder will remain on the floor framing layer

# Layout the Rafters

Extrude the **center** joist of the composite **ridge beam** to support the roof **rake**

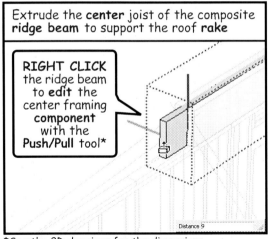

> **RIGHT CLICK** the ridge beam to **edit** the center framing **component** with the **Push/Pull** tool*

*See the 2D drawings for the dimensions

Lay out the **stringlines** for the roof framing in the **same** way as the **wall** framing

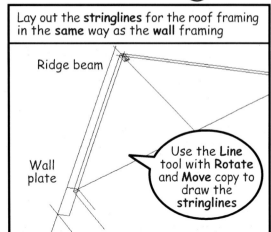

Ridge beam

Wall plate

> Use the **Line** tool with **Rotate** and **Move** copy to draw the **stringlines**

Using the 2D drawings as a reference, layout the **stringlines** for the **roof framing** and trim lines for the **rafter** at the **ridge beam** and **top plate** of the outside bearing wall**

Set the **bottom** of the rafter on the **top plate** to establish the height of the **ridge beam.**

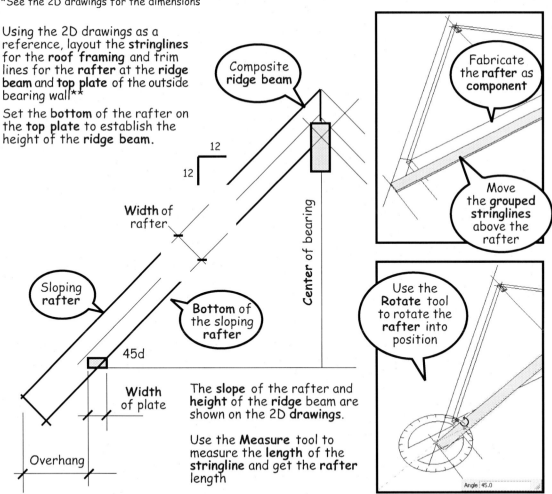

> Composite **ridge beam**

12
12

Width of rafter

Center of bearing

Sloping rafter

> Bottom of the sloping rafter

45d

Width of plate

Overhang

> Fabricate the **rafter** as **component**

> Move the **grouped stringlines** above the rafter

> Use the **Rotate** tool to rotate the **rafter** into position

Angle : 45.0

The **slope** of the rafter and **height** of the **ridge** beam are shown on the 2D **drawings.**

Use the **Measure** tool to measure the **length** of the **stringline** and get the **rafter** length

**Construct the framing diagram by drawing the 2D objects with the line tool, then ROTATE, MOVE and COPY into position

# 87

## Trim the Rafters

 V87Layout

The grouped **stringlines** act as guides above the rafters to mark the **trim lines** for the rafter at the **plate** and **ridge**

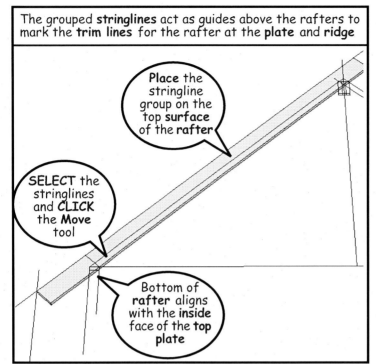

**Place** the stringline group on the top **surface** of the **rafter**

**SELECT** the stringlines and **CLICK** the **Move** tool

Bottom of **rafter** aligns with the **inside** face of the **top plate**

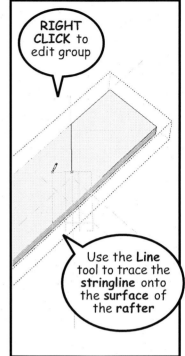

**RIGHT CLICK** to edit group

Use the **Line** tool to trace the **stringline** onto the **surface** of the rafter

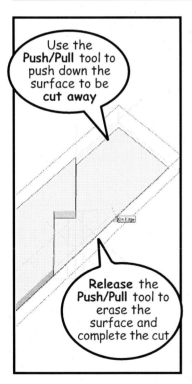

Use the **Push/Pull** tool to push down the surface to be **cut away**

**Release** the **Push/Pull** tool to erase the surface and complete the cut

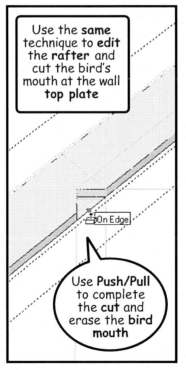

Use the **same** technique to **edit** the **rafter** and cut the bird's mouth at the wall **top plate**

Use **Push/Pull** to complete the **cut** and erase the **bird mouth**

**CLICK SAVE**

**Remember** to use Pages with Orbit, Zoom, Zoom Window, Pan and Undo View Change. These are **navigation tools** that speed the **modeling process.**

Add about **10 minutes** to get to this point in Step08.

Your actual **time** depends on how **intuitive** the modeling **process** is becoming.

## Place the Rafters

Rotate and place the rafter on the top plate of the north side of the span and use it to set the ridge beam

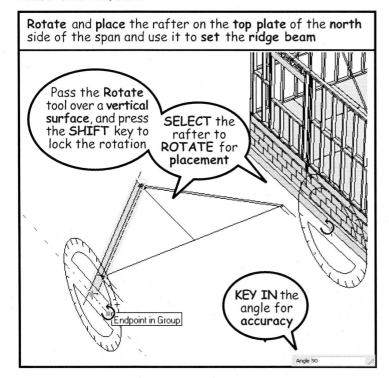

Pass the Rotate tool over a vertical surface, and press the SHIFT key to lock the rotation

SELECT the rafter to ROTATE for placement

KEY IN the angle for accuracy

Endpoint in Group

Angle 90

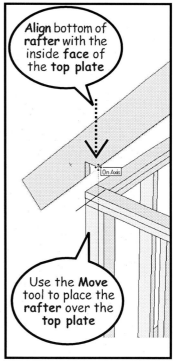

Align bottom of rafter with the inside face of the top plate

On Axis

Use the Move tool to place the rafter over the top plate

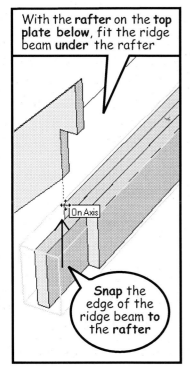

With the rafter on the top plate below, fit the ridge beam under the rafter

On Axis

Snap the edge of the ridge beam to the rafter

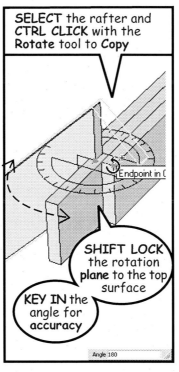

SELECT the rafter and CTRL CLICK with the Rotate tool to Copy

Endpoint in C

SHIFT LOCK the rotation plane to the top surface

KEY IN the angle for accuracy

Angle 180

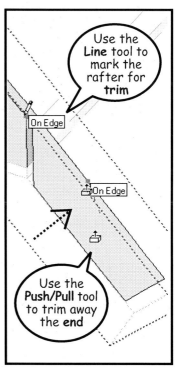

Use the Line tool to mark the rafter for trim

On Edge

On Edge

Use the Push/Pull tool to trim away the end

# Frame the Main Roof

 V89Rafter

With the **first** north and south **rafters** in place they can be copied as a **linear array** along the length of the **beam**

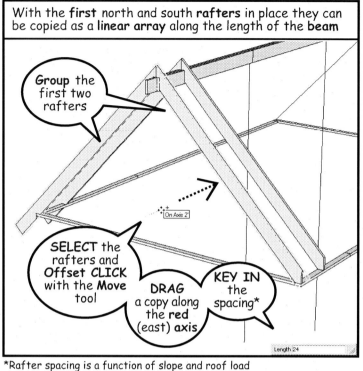

**Group** the first two rafters

**SELECT** the rafters and **Offset CLICK** with the **Move** tool

**DRAG** a copy along the **red** (east) **axis**

**KEY IN** the spacing*

On Axis 2'

Length 24

*Rafter spacing is a function of slope and roof load

Insert **full blocking** at **midspan** of the rafters

**Fabricate** a wood block the **depth** of the **rafters**

Midpoint Outside Active

Use the **Push/Pull** tool to size the **blocking** between the **rafters**

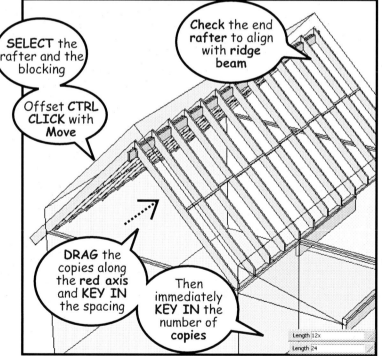

**SELECT** the rafter and the blocking

Offset **CTRL CLICK** with **Move**

**Check** the end **rafter** to align with **ridge beam**

**DRAG** the copies along the **red axis** and **KEY IN** the spacing

Then immediately **KEY IN** the number of **copies**

Length 12x
Length 24

⭐ CLICK SAVE

In **actual construction,** column and shear walls that support the roof must be calculated and **in place before** you place the ridge or **rafters.**

In a **construction model** you can place the **rafters first** and fit the ridge and walls **under** the rafters. Since there's **no gravity****

Figure another **10 minutes** to complete the rafters and get ready for the columns

230

90

**This makes the model a useful tool since you can measure and generate a cut list from the model

# Insert Roof Supports

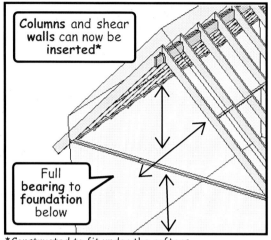

Columns and shear walls can now be inserted*

Full bearing to foundation below

*Constructed to fit under the rafters

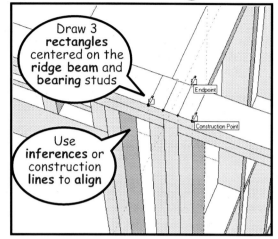

Draw 3 rectangles centered on the ridge beam and bearing studs

Use inferences or construction lines to align

Endpoint

Construction Point

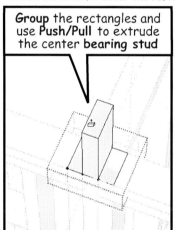

Group the rectangles and use Push/Pull to extrude the center bearing stud

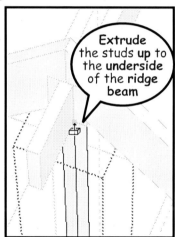

Extrude the studs up to the underside of the ridge beam

The three bearing studs act as a composite column

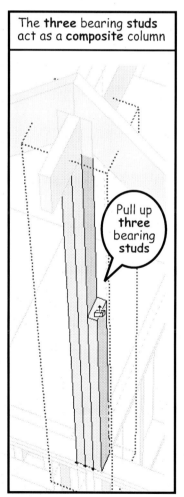

Pull up three bearing studs

Modify the length of a copy of Wall04 to fit under the ridge beam

The shear wall could also be a single wall

Ridge beam

Move a copy of Wall04 up as an extension of the shear wall

91

# Add the Fascia and Rake Overhang

Copy blocking and **insert** over perimeter **wall***

**Splice fascia** at rafter

Rotate and Edit a block to use as **fascia***

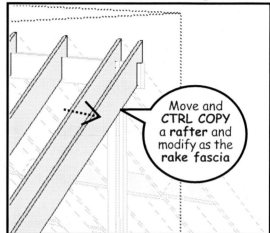

Move and **CTRL COPY** a **rafter** and modify as the **rake fascia**

*See 2D drawings for wall section

**Remove** the rafter's **bird mouth** to make the **rake**

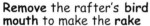

**CLICK** Edit Component and **connect** the **corners** with the **Line** tool

Endpoint

**Select** and **delete** extra lines

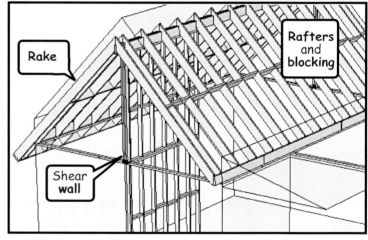

Rake

Rafters and blocking

Shear **wall**

Another **10 or so minutes** brings you to less than **4 hours** total program time (If all is going well)

Keep an eye on the clock and **conserve** your **minutes**

CLICK SAVE

240

Use the 2D drawings to **layout** the **stringlines*** for the shed **roof framing**. The rafters in this area span from the **top plate** of the outside wall to the **header beam** over the **interior** opening.

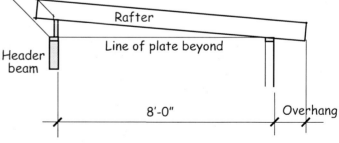

Line of main roof

Rafter

Line of plate beyond

Header beam

8'-0"

Overhang

**Construct the framing diagram by drawing the 2D objects, the Rotate, Move and Copy into position

92

# Layout and Frame the Shed Roof

Use the Line and Rectangle tools with **Move**, **Rotate**, and **Copy** to draw the **stringlines** in the lay out area

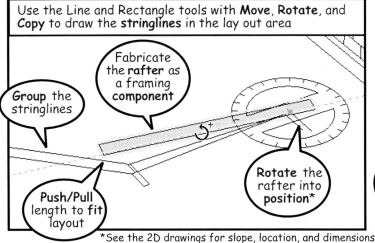

**Group** the stringlines

**Fabricate** the **rafter** as a framing **component**

**Rotate** the rafter into **position***

**Push/Pull** length to **fit** layout

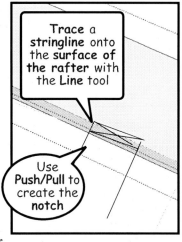

**Trace** a **stringline** onto the **surface of the rafter** with the Line tool

Use **Push/Pull** to create the **notch**

*See the 2D drawings for slope, location, and dimensions

Rotate and place the **first rafter** over the **corner** post

**Lower** rafter **attaches** to the **main** roof

SELECT and CTRL CLICK with **Move** to copy

KEY IN spacing

Length 24

KEY IN the **number** followed by an **X** to create multiple copies for the **linear array**

**Adjust** location of last **rafter**

Length 12x

Use **components** from main **roof**

**Add** blocking and **fascia**

93

## Layout the Gable Wall

To **fabricate** the **gable** walls use the **Measure** tool to measure the **opening** for construction in the **layout area**

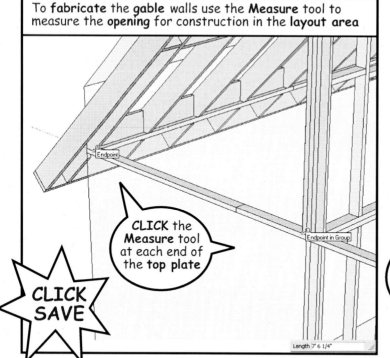

Endpoint

Endpoint in Group

> CLICK the **Measure** tool at each end of the **top plate**

**CLICK SAVE**

Length 7' 6 1/4"

Use **Zoom** and **Orbit** tools to **get into** tight spots

Endpoint

> To measure **CLICK** the **underside of rafter**

> CLICK at corner of the **Top plate**

Endpoint in Group

Length 7' 6 1/4"

---

Use the **measurements** taken from the wall and roof framing to lay out the **stringlines**

The **dimensions** of the opening are the **exact size** of the **triangular** opening. The **size** of the wall should be at least an **inch smaller** to allow for fit.

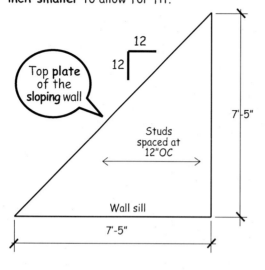

> Top **plate** of the **sloping** wall

12
12

Studs spaced at 12"OC

Wall sill

7'-5"

7'-5"

---

Make the Wall Framing layer active and use the **stringlines** to **fabricate** the **wall**

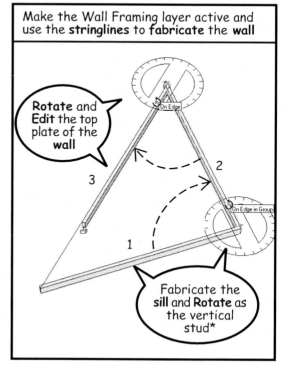

On Edge

> Rotate and Edit the top plate of the **wall**

3

2

1

On Edge in Group

> Fabricate the sill and **Rotate** as the vertical stud*

**94**  *Since there are only two of these gable ends, components are not necessary.

# Frame the Gable Wall

V94Gable

Lap the **framing** components at the corner of the **triangular wall** and edit to **fit**

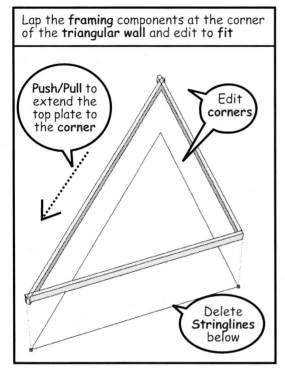

Push/Pull to extend the top plate to the **corner**

Edit **corners**

Delete **Stringlines** below

Use the **Line** tool to mark a **Push/Pull** plane

Then use the **Push/Pull** tool to edit the **component**

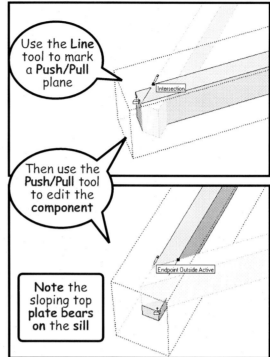

Intersection

Endpoint Outside Active

**Note** the sloping top plate **bears on** the sill

Use the **same** technique to edit the other corners. **RIGHT CLICK** to edit the group, **Line** tool to mark the trim, then use the Push/Pull tool to **push down** the gable **frame**

Push/ Pull

Line tool

Endpoint

Endpoint

Line tool

Line tool

Endpoint

**Note** the sloping top plate **bears on** the stud

Building a **triangular** frame in the field is **difficult** because it **has to fit** the **existing** opening.

CLICK SAVE

Sometimes this is **easier** to do **in place**, with each stud cut to fit the frame. This means a lot of measuring and fitting by the framers.

A **model** makes this **easier** since the pieces can be assembled and measured for preassembly

Figure another **10 minutes** to complete the rafters and the gable wall

250

# Place the Gable Wall

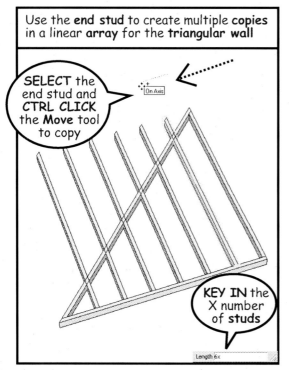

Use the **end stud** to create multiple **copies** in a linear **array** for the **triangular wall**

SELECT the end stud and CTRL CLICK the **Move** tool to copy

On Axis

KEY IN the X number of **studs**

Length 6x

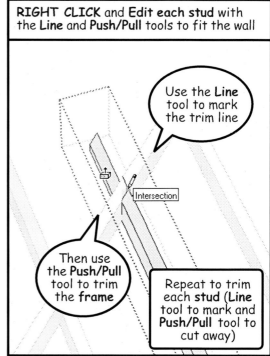

**RIGHT CLICK** and **Edit each stud** with the **Line** and **Push/Pull** tools to fit the wall

Use the **Line** tool to mark the trim line

Intersection

Then use the **Push/Pull** tool to trim the **frame**

Repeat to trim each **stud** (**Line** tool to mark and **Push/Pull** tool to cut away)

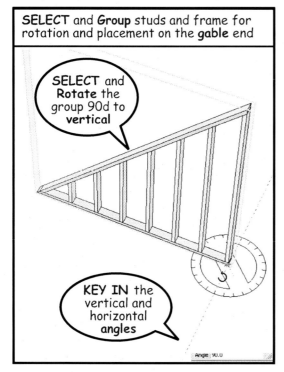

**SELECT** and **Group** studs and frame for rotation and placement on the **gable** end

SELECT and **Rotate** the group 90d to **vertical**

KEY IN the vertical and horizontal **angles**

Angle : 90.0

Use **Move** and **CTRL** to copy the **wall** to the **gable end**

**Move** tool

Endpoint

96

 V97Sheathing

Fabricate **roof sheathing** in the same way as the **floor sheathing** in Step06

**Stagger** the sheathing **horizontally**

**Start** the sheathing at the **midpoint** of the **rafter** for a **butt joint**

Edit the **sheathing** to fit the **ridge** and **rakes***

**Rotate** and place the sheathing on **both roofs**

Use the **Move** and **Rotate** tool with the **CTRL** key to create **copies**

Endpoint in Group

*Remember the transparent Zooms, Orbits, Pans and Pages to navigate

How did you do for time?

Add another **10 minutes** for the second gable wall for a total of about **50 minutes** for Step08.

The process should be getting more **intuitive**... right?

**RIGHT!**

CLICK SAVE

260

## DO YOU KNOW HOW TO:

1. Visualize the roof loads for the roof framing
2. Draw stringlines with the line and rectangle tools
3. Fabricate a wood block as a rafter component
4. Edit Just This One rafter to fit wall and ridge
5. Rotate, Move, CTRL Copy and array the rafters
6. Fabricate rafter blocking and insert into framing
7. Modify and place blocking component as fascia
8. Insert composite columns under the ridge beam
9. Insert a shear wall and adjust the stud heights
10. Fabricate roof sheathing and rotate and place

SAVE YOUR MINUTES

READY

OK, let's go to STEP09

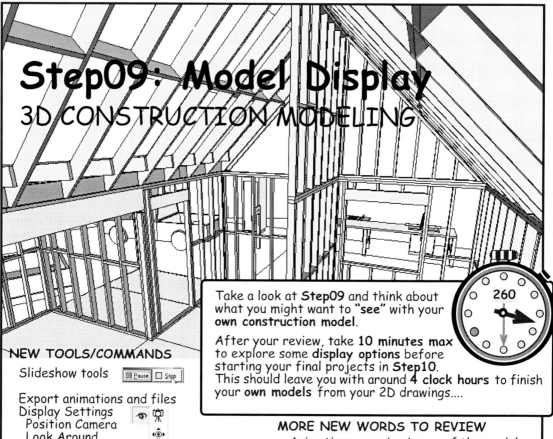

# Step09: Model Display
## 3D CONSTRUCTION MODELING

Take a look at **Step09** and think about what you might want to **"see"** with your **own construction model.**

After your review, take **10 minutes max** to explore some **display options** before starting your final projects in **Step10**. This should leave you with around **4 clock hours** to finish your **own models** from your 2D drawings....

260

## NEW TOOLS/COMMANDS

Slideshow tools

Export animations and files
Display Settings
  Position Camera
  Look Around
  Walk
  Zoom Field of View

Shade and Shadow
Print commands
SketchUp Resources

**User Forum**

## WHAT YOU WILL DO

1. SketchUp display options
2. Sequential process animations
3. Multiple Page slide shows
4. Export animations and images
5. Change the edges of objects

6. Camera placement using tripods

7. Set up shade and shadow options
8. Accelerator key command shortcuts

## MORE NEW WORDS TO REVIEW

Animation: a moving image of the model
AVI: a universal video file format
Delay time: the time the image displays
Drive-by: an animation at one eye height
Export: output a single or series of pages
Extensions: exaggerated corner lines
Eye Height: camera position above origin
Field of View: angle of perception
Fly by: an animation passing over the model
Hidden View: black and white model display
Jitter lines: jagged/sketchy object edges
Profile lines: outline of an object
Sequence animation: series of events
Slideshow: a series of displayed pages
Tourguide: SketchUp name for a slideshow
Transition time: the time between displays
Walk through: an animation along a path
Wireframe: display of just model edges
X-Ray: display with transparent surfaces

# Overview of Model Display Options

Use the model to **animate events** or **illustrate** details. The **Pages** set up views. **Display Options** adjust the image. **Camera tools** position the point of view for export or print.

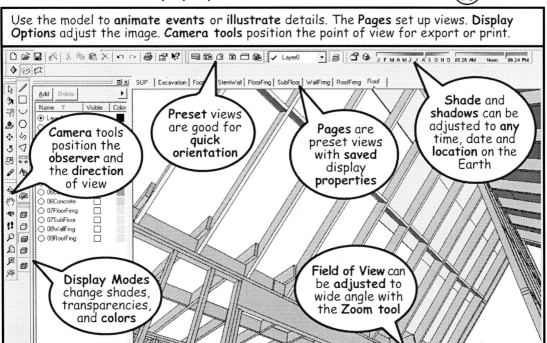

**Camera** tools position the **observer** and the **direction** of view

**Preset** views are good for **quick orientation**

**Pages** are preset views with **saved** display **properties**

**Shade** and **shadows** can be adjusted to **any** time, date and **location** on the Earth

**Display Modes** change shades, transparencies, and **colors**

**Field of View** can be **adjusted** to wide angle with the **Zoom tool**

An **animation** is a **series** of pages with different objects hidden or **layers** turned on or off to help **visualize** the construction **process**. This is a **series** of framed model images

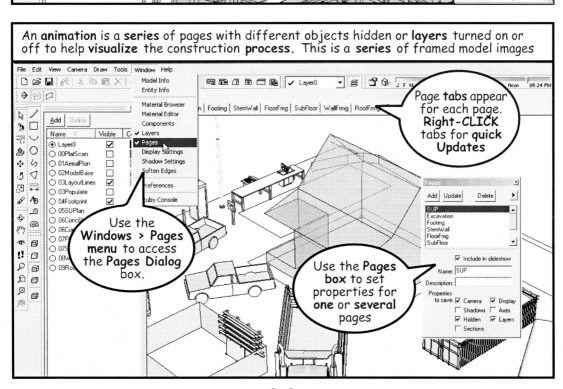

**Page tabs** appear for each page. **Right-CLICK** tabs for **quick Updates**

Use the **Windows > Pages** menu to access the **Pages Dialog** box.

Use the **Pages box** to set properties for **one** or **several** pages

## Sequence Animations

To set up a **series** of pages from a **single point of view\*** as a sequence animation of the construction process:

1. Use **File > Save As** to save a unique file for the animation.

2. **Adjust** layer **visibility** and hide/unhide objects

3. Add the **first Page** with the Windows > Pages menu. **Right CLICK** a Page Tab to add future pages or **Update** adjustments

4. **Repeat** for each page in the animation **sequence**

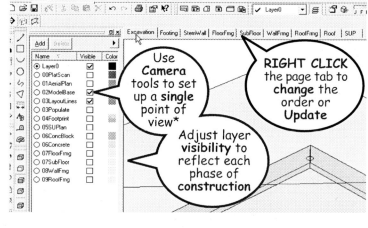

V100Slides

Use **Camera** tools to set up a **single point of view\***

**RIGHT CLICK** the page tab to **change** the order or **Update**

Adjust layer **visibility** to reflect each phase of **construction**

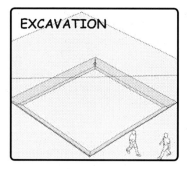
EXCAVATION

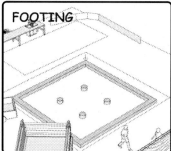
FOOTING

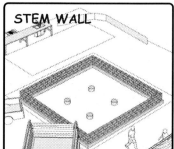
STEM WALL

FLOOR FRAMING

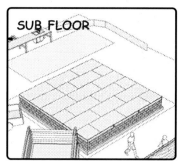
SUB FLOOR

WALL FRAMING

ROOF FRAMING

ROOFING

WORK PLAN

\*A single point of view is important to keep the animation and viewer focused on the process

Once setup, the pages can be **played** automatically in sequential order as a slideshow. The **controller** allows the slides to be **paused** for comment or **played** at different speeds.

SELECT the **View>Tourguide** menu to play the **Slideshow**

The **slideshow** dialog box appears as a **controller**

The slideshow **begins** with the current **page** and continues until you stop

The **Tourguide settings** can also be used to **change** the time the slide is **displayed** and the **transition time** between slides. Longer transitions can **smooth** the animation

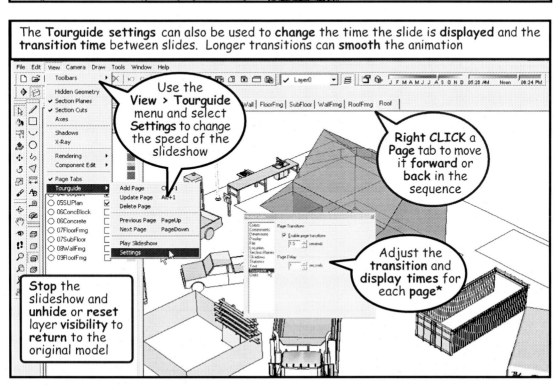

Use the **View > Tourguide** menu and select **Settings** to change the speed of the slideshow

Right CLICK a **Page** tab to move it **forward** or **back** in the sequence

Adjust the **transition** and display **times** for each **page***

**Stop** the slideshow and **unhide** or **reset** layer **visibility** to **return** to the original model

*Note that many other preferences can also be changed, we'll look at some of these later

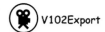
Once the sequence and timing are set up, the **completed slideshow** can be exported as a **animation** that can be played by almost **any media player** or presentation program.

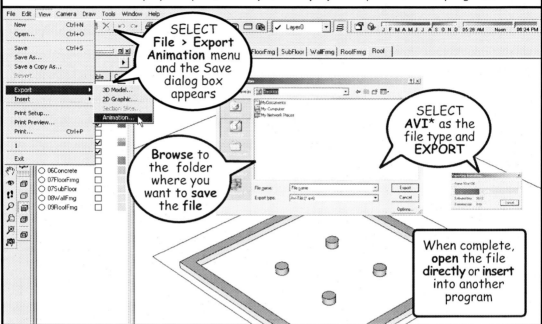

SELECT **File > Export Animation** menu and the Save dialog box appears

**Browse** to the folder where you want to **save** the file

SELECT **AVI*** as the file type and **EXPORT**

When complete, **open** the file **directly** or **insert** into another program

*AVI files are compressed image files similar to JPEGs

You can export a **2D Graphic** in a variety of file types. This **includes** JPEG, BMP, and TIF **bitmaps** that can be **inserted** into presentation, word processing, and spreadsheet **programs**.

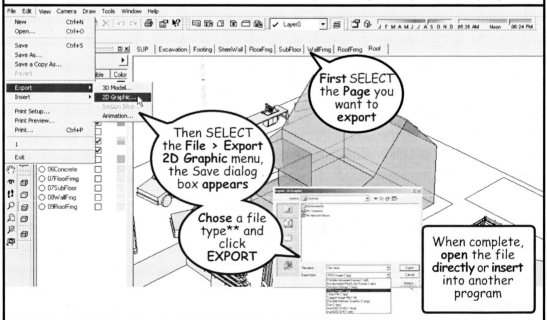

**First** SELECT the **Page** you want to **export**

Then SELECT the **File > Export 2D Graphic** menu, the Save dialog box **appears**

**Chose** a file type** and click **EXPORT**

When complete, **open** the file **directly** or **insert** into another program

**JPEGs are small and can be emailed or inserted into most programs.

**TIFs and BMPs are higher resolution and good for prints and posters from commercial printers

# Line or Edge Display Options

The **Display Modes toolbar** and **Display Settings** dialog box change the way the model **appears** on a Page or slideshow. Keep it clear and simple

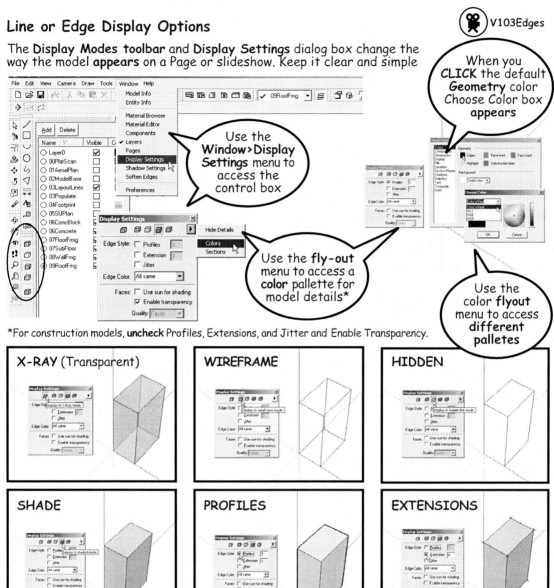

> When you **CLICK** the default **Geometry** color Choose Color box **appears**

> Use the **Window>Display Settings** menu to access the control box

> Use the **fly-out** menu to access a **color** pallette for model details*

> Use the color **flyout** menu to access **different palletes**

*For construction models, **uncheck** Profiles, Extensions, and Jitter and Enable Transparency.

## X-RAY (Transparent)

## WIREFRAME

## HIDDEN

## SHADE

## PROFILES

## EXTENSIONS

## JITTER

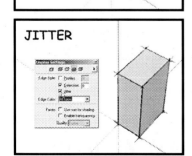

## SUN SHADING

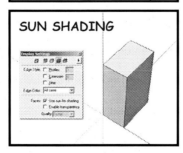

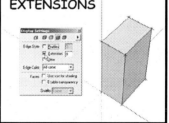

The **Display Settings** can be checked **individually** or in **combination** with each other to get the desired effect.

Remember to **update** the **Pages** for **new settings**.

Also keep it simple, remember this is a **construction model** and not about design

103

## Camera and Viewpoint Options

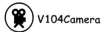
V104Camera

**Camera Tools** are used to **position** the **observer** relative to the model. They can be used in **combination** to set up virtually any view so that it can be **added** as a **Page** or part of a **series** of pages in a **slideshow**. This includes **fly-bys**, **drive-bys**, **walk-throughs**, and other **animations**.

### Camera Tools (again)

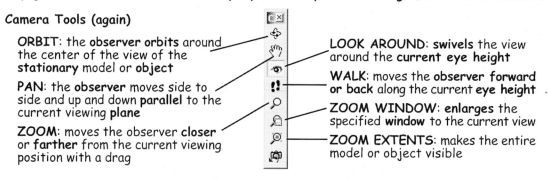

**ORBIT**: the **observer orbits** around the center of the view of the **stationary** model or **object**

**PAN**: the **observer** moves side to side and up and down **parallel** to the current viewing **plane**

**ZOOM**: moves the observer **closer** or **farther** from the current viewing position with a drag

**LOOK AROUND**: **swivels** the view around the **current eye height**

**WALK**: moves the **observer forward** or **back** along the current **eye height**

**ZOOM WINDOW**: **enlarges** the specified **window** to the current view

**ZOOM EXTENTS**: makes the entire model or object visible

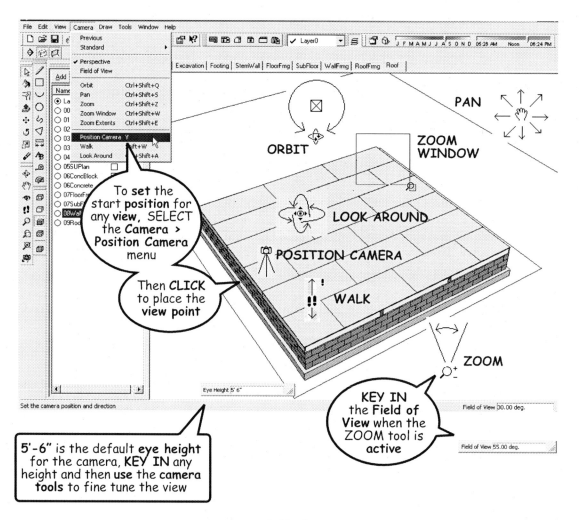

To **set** the start **position** for any **view**, SELECT the Camera > Position Camera menu

Then **CLICK** to place the **view point**

PAN

ORBIT

ZOOM WINDOW

LOOK AROUND

POSITION CAMERA

WALK

ZOOM

KEY IN the **Field of View** when the ZOOM tool is active

Field of View 30.00 deg.

Field of View 55.00 deg.

**5'-6"** is the default **eye height** for the camera, KEY IN any height and then **use** the **camera tools** to fine tune the view

104

 V104Camera

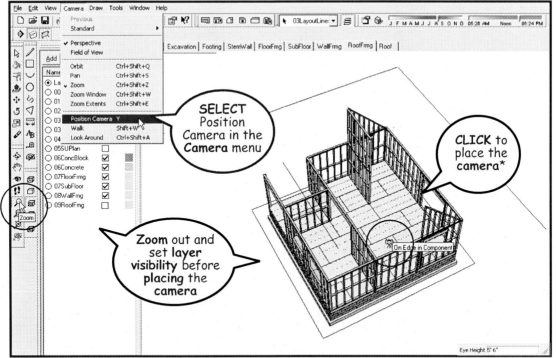

SELECT Position Camera in the **Camera** menu

CLICK to place the camera*

**Zoom** out and set layer **visibility** before **placing** the camera

On Edge in Component

Eye Height 5'6"

*The default camera "eye height" is 5'-6" above the elevation of the point of the click.

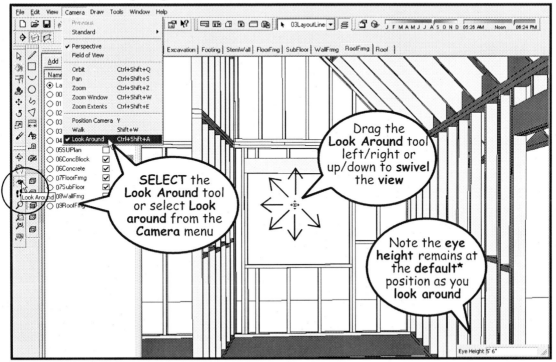

Drag the **Look Around** tool left/right or up/down to **swivel** the **view**

SELECT the **Look Around** tool or select **Look around** from the **Camera** menu

Note the **eye height** remains at the **default*** position as you **look around**

Eye Height 5'6"

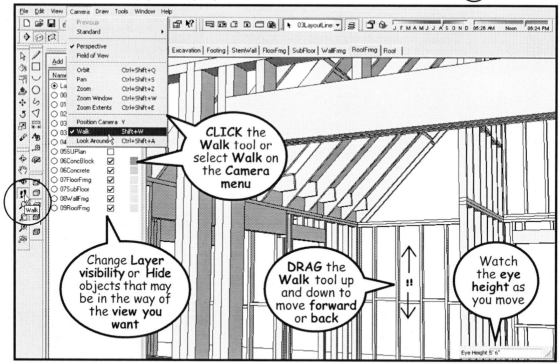

\*The default value is 30 degrees. The higher the number the wider the view. You can also DRAG with the SHIFT key held down to change

Use **layer** visibility, **Hide/Unhide** objects, and the **Camera and Display tools** to position the observer point of view and **emphasize** particular parts or aspects of the **model**. **Images** can then be exported as a single view or slideshow for comments and notations.

# Special Animations from Controlled Viewpoints

Make a **slideshow** that looks like a fly-by, drive-by, or walk-through by setting up a **series of Pages** based on a number of **evenly spaced "tripods"** all aiming at the same model **target**

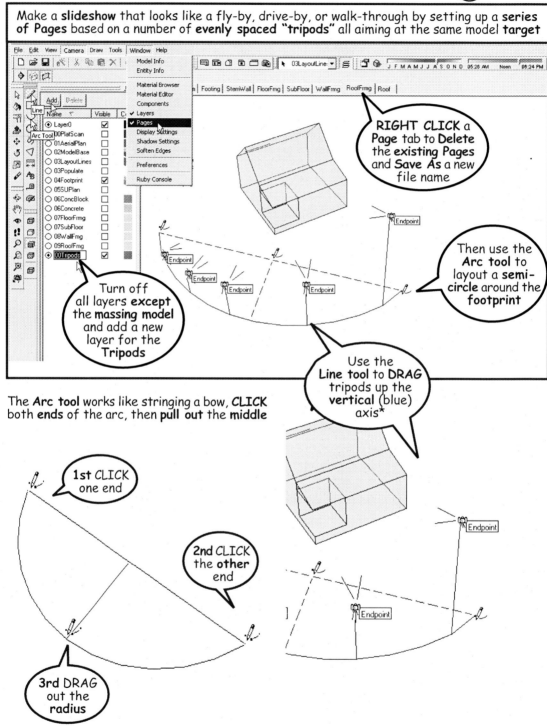

The **Arc tool** works like stringing a bow, **CLICK** both **ends** of the arc, then **pull out** the middle

1st CLICK one end

2nd CLICK the other end

3rd DRAG out the radius

RIGHT CLICK a Page tab to Delete the existing Pages and Save As a new file name

Then use the Arc tool to layout a semi-circle around the footprint

Turn off all layers except the massing model and add a new layer for the Tripods

Use the Line tool to DRAG tripods up the vertical (blue) axis*

108

*The closer and more evenly spaced the tripods, the smoother the slide show animation

## Layout the Fly-by Sequence

V108FlyBy

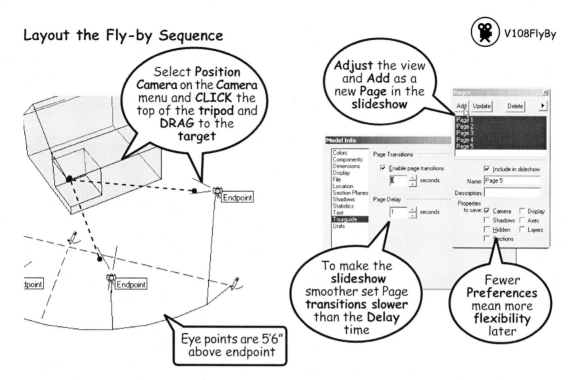

Select **Position Camera** on the **Camera** menu and **CLICK** the top of the **tripod** and **DRAG** to the **target**

**Adjust** the view and **Add** as a new **Page** in the slideshow

To make the **slideshow** smoother set Page **transitions slower** than the **Delay** time

Fewer **Preferences** mean more **flexibility** later

Eye points are 5'6" above endpoint

When the **tripods** are **ready** and the Pages are roughly set up, **turn off** the **footprint** layer and make the objects and layers **visible** that you want to see in the final animation. **RIGHT CLICK** the Page Tab to **adjust** Preferences and **Update** as you **make changes**.

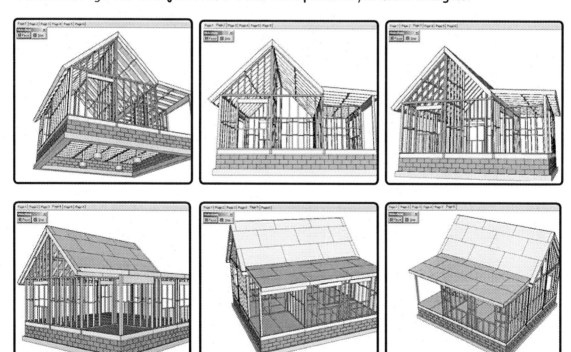

109

## Adding Shade and Shadow

**Shade and shadows** can be added to **any view** and saved as part of **Page preferences**.

This feature has **limited** application for construction models because it can **confuse** construction information and **details** with design features.

However **some** applications may be **important**. For example, illustrate solar **exposure** or **day light** for **materials** and special installations during construction.

This makes the model an **analytical tool** for **planning work** and scheduling daily activities.

___

**Start** by setting up the **view point** with the layers and object you want **visible**

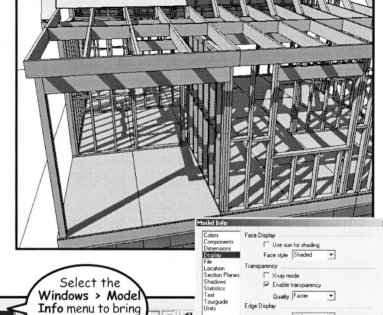

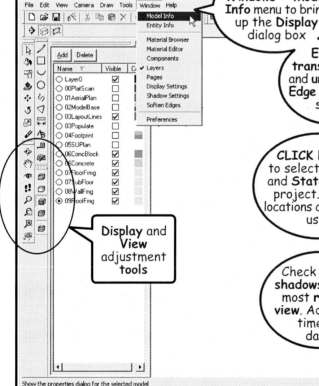

Select the **Windows > Model Info** menu to bring up the **Display** dialog box

**Enable transparency** and **uncheck** all **Edge Styles** to start

**Display** and **View** adjustment tools

**CLICK** location to select the **City** and **State** for the project. Custom locations can **also** be used

Check **Display shadows** for the most **realistic** view. Adjust the time and date*

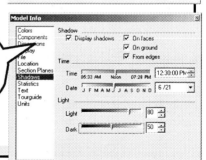

*Shade and shadow adjustments can also be made dynamically with the Shade and Shadow Toolbar

# Printer Controls and Hard Copy Output

To **Print** a file use the **File** > **Print Setup**, **Print Preview** and **Print** menu. Though most model images are **exported** as **JPEGs** and inserted into text, spreadsheet, web page, or slideshows, **prints** are also **necessary** as paper documents,

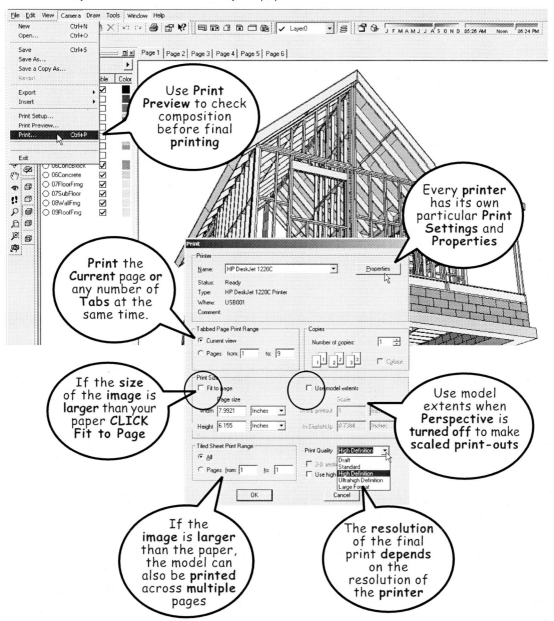

Use **Print Preview** to check composition before final **printing**

Every **printer** has its own particular **Print Settings** and **Properties**

**Print** the **Current** page **or** any number of **Tabs** at the same time.

If the **size** of the **image** is **larger** than your paper **CLICK Fit to Page**

Use model extents when **Perspective** is **turned off** to make scaled print-outs

If the **image** is **larger** than the paper, the model can also be **printed** across **multiple** pages

The **resolution** of the final print **depends** on the resolution of the **printer**

Color ink is **expensive** and colors often **bleed** together on ink jet printers. For the best quality print **Export** the file as a **2D TIF** or **BMP** and take the file to a **professional** copy and printing service. Large format prints are great as **posters** or **displays** and **exhibits**.

111

## Shortcut and Key Commands

Keyboard **Shortcuts** accelerate modeling and **eliminate** most **menu** and **toolbar** mouse clicks

Many common **menu** and **toolbar commands** can be found in **Shortcut** Preferences

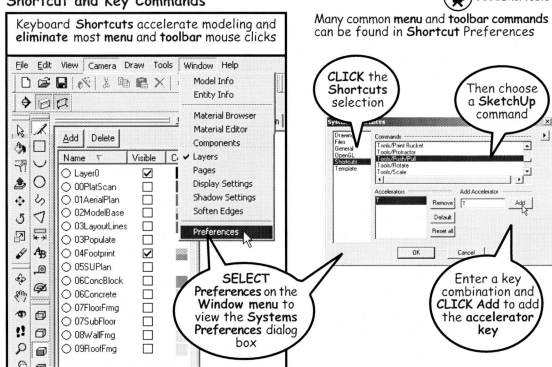

**CLICK** the **Shortcuts** selection

Then choose a **SketchUp** command

**SELECT Preferences** on the **Window menu** to view the **Systems Preferences** dialog box

Enter a key combination and **CLICK Add** to add the **accelerator** key

Keep in mind that you only need shortcuts for the **most common** commands. In fact, the **easiest way** to **add** them is **one at a time** (as you use them). Also note that **one hand** is almost always on the mouse while the other is **free** to **press** a key. Placing the shortcuts on one side of the keyboard will be more efficient*. Here are some suggestions for a **right handed mouse**:

| | |
|---|---|
| Camera/Look Around | Ctrl+Shift+A |
| Camera/Orbit | Ctrl+Shift+Q |
| Camera/Pan | Ctrl+Shift+S |
| Camera/Position Camera | Y |
| Camera/Previous | Shift+Z |
| Camera/Walk | Ctrl+Shift+W |
| Camera/Zoom | Ctrl+Shift+Z |
| Camera/Zoom Extents | Ctrl+Shift+E |
| Camera/Zoom Window | Ctrl+Shift+W |
| | |
| Draw/Arc | A |
| Draw/Circle | C |
| Draw/Line | W |
| Draw/Rectangle | R |
| | |
| Edit/Construction/Erase | Alt+E |
| Edit/Copy | Ctrl+C |
| Edit/Cut | Ctrl+X |
| Edit/Erase | Backspace |
| Edit/Hide | H |
| Edit/Make Group | G |
| Edit/Paste | Ctrl+V |
| Edit/Redo | Ctrl+Y |
| Edit/Select/All | Ctrl+A |
| Edit/Undo | Ctrl+Z |
| Edit/Unhide/All | Ctrl+H |

| | |
|---|---|
| Edit/Unhide/Last | Alt+H |
| Edit/Unhide/Selected | Ctrl+H |
| | |
| File/New | Ctrl+N |
| File/Open | Ctrl+O |
| File/Print | Ctrl+P |
| File/Save | Ctrl+S |
| | |
| Tools/Aves | Alt+A |
| Tools/Dimensions | D |
| Tools/Eraser | E |
| Tools/Measure | F |
| Tools/Move | B |
| Tools/Offset | V |
| Tools/Paint Bucket | Alt+B |
| Tools/Push Pull | T |
| Tools/Rotate | R |
| Tools/Scale | S |
| Tools/Select | Space bar |
| Tools/Text | Alt+W |
| | |
| View/Tourguide/Add Page | Ctrl+1 |
| View/Tourguide/Next Page | Page Down |
| View/Tourguide/Previous Page | Page Up |
| View/Tourguide/Update Page | Alt+1 |

*To remind you, the shortcuts appear on the menus next to the commands after they are assigned

## Other Learning Resources

The most important **HELP** resource in this program is on the **SketchUp Website\***

SELECT Help>SketchUp Website to access the **User Forum**

**Search** first, then **Ask** a question on this open **forum** and you will be amazed at the **expert response**

This is also a **good time** to review the **Written** and **Video** tutorials **you skipped...**

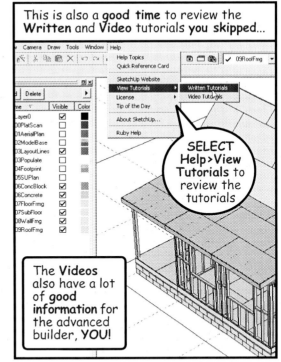

SELECT Help>View Tutorials to review the tutorials

The **Videos** also have a lot of **good information** for the advanced builder, **YOU!**

\*You must be online to access

### DO YOU KNOW HOW TO:

1. Use display options to position the model and observer
2. Navigate to a viewpoint and add/update a Page
3. Control object's visibility in a series of Pages
4. View a series of Pages as a slideshow or tourguide
5. Export movies to be played in other programs
6. Export individual Page images as bitmap files
7. Change eye height and field of view in a display
8. Change edge display to give different effects
9. Place cameras on tripods to control point of view
10. Set time and location for shade and shadow
11. Create key commands to speed model construction
12. Access SketchUp learning resources

**Save** your model **As a** new file and take **ten minutes** to **try** some of the display options.

**Watch** your **minutes** carefully, you will need them for **Step10**

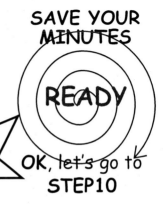

SAVE YOUR MINUTES

READY

CLICK SAVE

OK, let's go to STEP10

113

# Step10: Your Turn
## 3D CONSTRUCTION MODELING

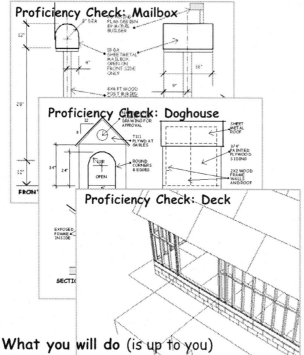

Proficiency Check: Mailbox

Proficiency Check: Doghouse

Proficiency Check: Deck

You should have around **4 hours remaining** at this point, but continue to **conserve** your minutes. If you're getting **serious** about the **potential** of this tool, you also need to consider buying this **great program**.

**CLICK SAVE**

OK, it's your **TURN**

**READY**

**SAVE YOUR MINUTES**

### What you will do (is up to you)

Here's a chance to practice what you've learned and strike out on your own with your own project.

**Mailbox**: is a quick proficiency check just to hone your plan reading skills and let you practice all the commands you should now know.

**Doghouse** is closer to the real world (of dogs). Here's a minimal design drawing where you have to figure out the construction and show how you would build the model (in sequence).

**The Deck** is a design-build project for the model you completed in the book. The idea is to design and build a deck for the back patio of the house.

**All these projects** require **thinking** through the construction **before starting** the work. **Some** require **more** thinking than others -- just like the real world.

*The **shorties for Step10** are on the "Instructors CD" or if you are a self learner, CLICK the **email request** on the companion CD in the back of this book and we will email you a **download link**.

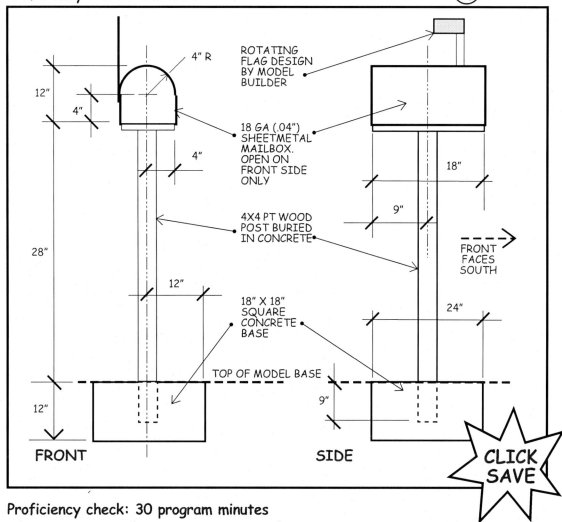

ROTATING
FLAG DESIGN
BY MODEL
BUILDER

4" R

12"

4"

4"

18 GA (.04")
SHEETMETAL
MAILBOX.
OPEN ON
FRONT SIDE
ONLY

4X4 PT WOOD
POST BURIED
IN CONCRETE

28"

18"

9"

FRONT
FACES
SOUTH

12"

18" X 18"
SQUARE
CONCRETE
BASE

24"

TOP OF MODEL BASE

12"

9"

FRONT

SIDE

CLICK SAVE

## Proficiency check: 30 program minutes

Using **only** the information shown on the 2D drawing above, build a **3D model** with the following **minimum criteria**.

1. At least **5 layers** with these RGB colors*:
   a. Model base (150/100/50) 50% transparent
   b. Wood post (240/230/140)
   c. Sheetmetal mailbox (190/190/190)
   d. Concrete (234/234/234) 75% transparent
   e. Flag and pin (255/0/0)

2. Show **construction lines** to place the mail box at 15'-6" south and 3'-6" east of a **WORKPOINT** in your model base

3. Excavate using 45 degree **angle of repose**, no stockpile necessary

*Turn on Color by Layer

4. Turn on **Shade and Shadow** set for 3pm, 22 October, in Yuma, Arizona

5. Export at least one **close up** Page view from the **south** with Extensions lines and Profiles and Jitter turned **off**

## SAVE YOUR MINUTES

**TIP**: Preconstruction is important in any building. **Think** through the process before **you jump** in and **start** building (anything).

# Proficiency Check: Construction Model

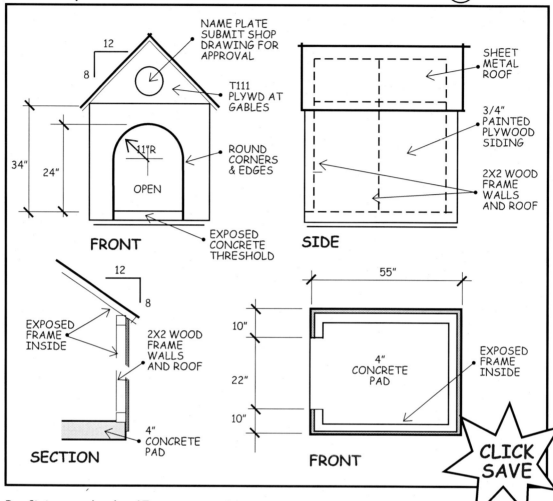

NAME PLATE
SUBMIT SHOP
DRAWING FOR
APPROVAL

12
8

T111
PLYWD AT
GABLES

ROUND
CORNERS
& EDGES

11"R

34"    24"

OPEN

FRONT

EXPOSED
CONCRETE
THRESHOLD

SHEET
METAL
ROOF

3/4"
PAINTED
PLYWOOD
SIDING

2X2 WOOD
FRAME
WALLS
AND ROOF

SIDE

12
8

EXPOSED
FRAME
INSIDE

2X2 WOOD
FRAME
WALLS
AND ROOF

4"
CONCRETE
PAD

SECTION

55"

10"

22"

10"

4"
CONCRETE
PAD

EXPOSED
FRAME
INSIDE

FRONT

CLICK
SAVE

## Proficiency check: 45 program minutes

Using the information shown on the design drawing above, build a 3D **construction model** as a **slideshow** showing the sequence of construction.

Your model should include a **minimum** of:

1. A model **base** with a **WORKPOINT**
2. **Excavation** and **concrete** foundation
3. **Framing** for wall and roof
4. Plywood **siding** and gable ends
5. Name plate (shop drawing required)

Since this is a **construction** model, display should show **no** shade/shadows, profiles, edges, or jitter lines

**SAVE AS** and delete the model you built in Steps 01 - 08 and use its layers and colors and save time*.

Program time should be kept to a **minimum** so be sure to **plan your sequence carefully**.

## SAVE YOUR MINUTES

**TIP**: **Think** through the model process **before** you start **building**. Have a plan before you open the program to start construction.

345

116

*Turnon  Color by Layer

YourTurn

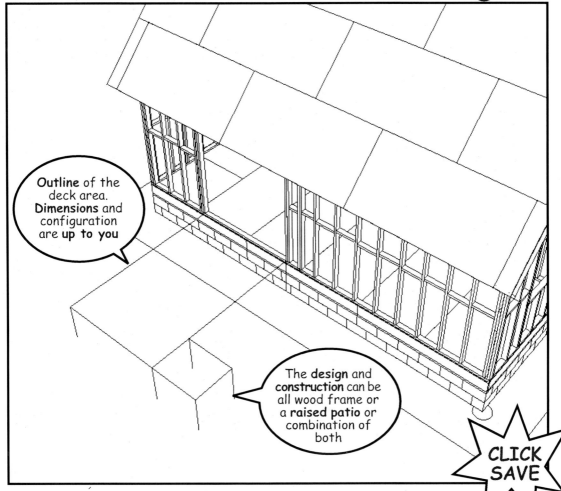

Outline of the deck area. **Dimensions** and configuration are **up to you**

The **design** and **construction** can be all wood frame or a **raised patio** or combination of both

CLICK SAVE

## Proficiency check: 60 program minutes

The floor **elevation** at the **back** of the house means that a raised **deck or patio** needs to be constructed with steps down to a garden.

The **design is up to you**, but the following should be considered required in the **final** model construction:

1. Rough **field drawings** to show what you are planning to build before you start.

2. A **sequence model** showing the phases of construction coordinated with the **phases** of construction for the main house.

3. Design, materials, and framing techniques to **match the main house**.

4. Present your completed model as an **exported** 6 -10 step drive-by **animation AND** at least two full color (by layer) **JPEG files** ready for professional printing.

## SAVE YOUR MINUTES

**TIP: Think** through the design and construction process **off-line** before you start building. In construction you always have a plan **before** you start.

117

YourTurn

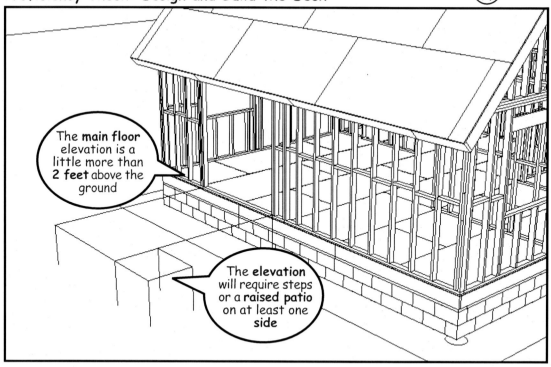

118

## Review What You Learned

### Now you know how to design and build a 3D Construction Model:

**STEP 01:**
You know how to insert a plat map and build a 3D model base

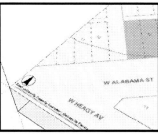

**STEP 02:**
You can scale the site to the real world and layout the construction

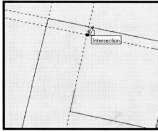

**STEP 03:**
You can draw the site conditions and setbacks and complete a Work Plan

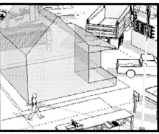

**STEP 04:**
You know how to excavate for the foundation from a workpoint

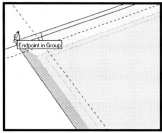

**STEP 05:**
You know how to form and pour footings and build a concrete block wall

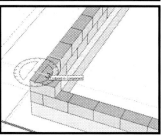

**STEP 06:**
You can frame the floor sills, joists and sheathing

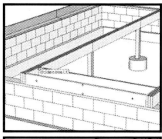

**STEP 07:** You know how to frame the stud walls and place the top plates

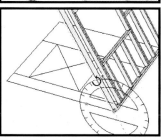

**STEP 08:** You know how to complete the roof framing and support members

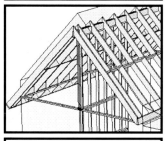

**STEP 09:**
You can change views of the model and create animations

**STEP 10:**
And you proved you can design and build anything

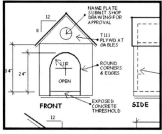

119

# GLOSSARY

**Words from this books you now know:**

2D Drawings: usually including plans, elevations, sections, and details
2D Footprint: the perimeter of the building at the foundation line
3D Axes: Red, Green, Blue axes in SketchUp, X,Y,Z axes in CAD
3D Footprint: a 3D massing model giving the shape of the building
Aerial map: public tax survey map usually found at local government offices
Angle of repose: slope of the earth on the side of an excavation
Animation: a moving image of the model as a movie or AVI file
Array: circular or linear row of copies generated automatically
AVI: is a video file format that can be viewed with most media players
Axis: A line that defines the north, south, or vertical axis of 3D space
Backfill: the compacted material that fills an excavation after framing
Beam pockets: placement of bearing points in the wall framing
Bearing stud: structural framing members under load
Bearing wall: structural framing assembly under load
Bearing: concentration point of a structural load from above
Bird mouth: a notch cut into a framing member at the point of bearing
Block: 8x8x16 hollow concrete masonry unit
Block: a basic shape of wood or concrete for further fabrication
Blocking: a structural framing member that fits between joists or studs
BMP file: an uncompressed high resolution graphic file format

CLICK: quick press and release of the left mouse button
Component: prefabricated piece of a model, independent of other objects
Composite beam: field fabricated beam composed of multiple framing joists
Composite column: field fabricated column composed of multiple framing studs
Construction lines: SketchUp name for temporary layout lines
Construction Model: an analytical visualization tool built as an assembly
Context menu: command or object specific menu accessed with a RIGHT CLICK
Corner stud: a stud placed at the intersection of a stud wall as a nailer
Cripple: a short piece of stud placed above or below an opening
Delay time: the time a Page image displays before it transitions to a new Page
DOUBLE CLICK: two quick CLICKS of the left mouse button
Download: transfer a file from a server or network to your computer
DRAG: press and hold mouse button as you move the cursor
Drainage plan: is necessary to protect adjacent property from water run off
Drive-by: the view of a moving observer from one eye height

Eave: The lower overhang of a sloping roof
Excavation: the hole made when the earth is removed for foundation
Export: generating a file of a model image as a single or series of pages
Extensions: SketchUp corner and edge lines extended beyond an intersection
Extrude: act of elongating a 2D shape with SketchUp's Push Pull tool
Eye Height: the height of the camera view point above its origin

# GLOSSARY

## Words from this book you now know:

Fabrication process: a sequence of steps to fabricate a piece of construction
Fascia: the eave or lower edge of rafters of sloping roof
Field of View: the width or angle of view from the eye of the observer
Fly by: the view of a moving observer passing by the model at various eye heights
Footer: another word for a footing in common usage
Footing: a concrete bearing pad or continuous concrete under a stem wall
Foundation: a bearing system includes footings, stem walls, slabs, and reinforcing
Framing: an assembly of structural members or pieces as a system

Girder: large supporting beam in the floor framing system
Group: a collection of surfaces and edges as a single model object
Half block: a "split" or 8" x 8" x 8" concrete block
Header: a horizontal load bearing member above an opening
Hidden View: black and white model display, good for further annotation
Hot spot: active point of a cursor CLICK or object selection
Inference: SketchUp modeling hints visible as a reference to cursor position
Installer: a self executing file that loads a program onto your computer
Jack stud: support stud or trimmer under a door header
Jamb: support stud or trimmer under a window header
Jitter lines: jagged/sketchy object edges in SketchUP
Joists: equally spaced floor or ceiling framing member
JPEG: a compact compression format for a graphics file

KEY IN: direct input from the keyboard without clicking
King stud: full length stud on outside of a trimmer or jamb
Lay down area: designated work area for preassembly and preparation
Layer: a way to separate objects in model space
Lumber: wood milled to stock sizes as framing members
Massing model: 3D outline of the building to aid in visualization
Morph: transform from one shape to another

Nailer: framing member placed for attachment of some material
Nominal: the listed size, not actual size, of construction materials
North: geographic or solar north on a survey, not plan north
Object: a Group of lines and surfaces that can be viewed in 3D
Origin: the intersection of the three axes in model space
Overhang: extended portion of the roof at the eave or rake

Page View: user saved views of the model and display properties
Palette: a collection of tools with a common use or purpose
Perimeter: outside face of foundation wall or the 2D footprint
Pier: short column for a concentrated load at the foundation

# GLOSSARY

## Words from this book you now know:

Plan North: reference north in model space, not geographic north
Plat map: a tax or assessor's map that shows property lines
Plate: a horizontal framing member in a stud wall
Plumb-line: line perpendicular to the horizon used to reference vertical
Post: vertical support column in the framing system
Profile lines: the outline or outer edges of an object in SketchUp
Property boundaries: limits of the ownership and the work plan
Protractor: measures degrees of an angle in the rotation command
Pull Down menus: additional options found in many SketchUp dialog boxes

Rafters: usually sloping framing members for a roof
Rake: the sloping edge of a roof
Red, Green, Blue Axes: SketchUp's name for the X, Y, and Z axes in CAD
RGB: the red, green, blue color mixing palette in many color programs
Ridge beam: the upper most framing beam supports the rafters
Ridge: the high point of a roof usually defined by the ridge beam
RIGHT CLICK: a CLICK with the right mouse button
Right/Left selection: everything inside and touched by the selection box
Rotate cursor: the protractor at the tip of the cursor for the Rotate tool

Scale bar: graphic distance indicator on a plat or aerial map
Scan: a BMP file created by a copy scanner
Sense of scale: objects inserted in a model to help visualize construction
Sequence animation: a series of phased events from a single point of view
Setbacks: the legal limits of the finished building construction
Shear wall: a structural wall that absorbs lateral loads
Sheathing: a flat surface material to fit on floor, wall, and roof framing
SHIFT LOCK: constrains the rotation tool to the plane of an object
Sill: the lowest member of a framing system
Simulation: representation of a construction process in a model sequence
Slideshow: a series of displayed pages in SketchUp
Slope: the pitch or angle of the roof
Solid object: group of lines and surfaces that are independent in a model
Stagger: off set pattern for attaching sheathing or other framing members
Staging area: designated storage area for preassembly and preparation
Stem wall: foundation wall built on a footing
Stringlines: a reference line for construction layout
Stud: the equally spaced vertical members in a framed wall
Subfloor: flooring sheathing laid on the floor framing joists
SUP: site utilization plan or work plan for construction
Surface: surface in SketchUp is separate from its edges
Survey stake: is a reference mark set by surveyor to check elevation

# GLOSSARY

## Words from this book you now know:

Temporary power: electrical utility installed just for the construction
TIFF: a high resolution BMP file used by professional printers
Toe of slope: bottom of the excavation's angle of repose or cut in earth
Tools: Toolbar and menu utilities on the SketchUp interface
Top of slope: top of the excavation's angle of repose or cut in earth
Tourguide: SketchUp name for a slideshow
Transition time: the time between Page displays
Transparent: use of a tool when another tool is active
Trimmer: or jack stud, supports the header of an opening in the framing
Truss system: load bearing frame defines the ceiling and roof

Valley: the inside angle of a roof slope change
Value Control Box: the SketchUp indicator in the lower right corner
Vertical reference: off set reference of change in elevation
Visibility: Temporarily hide or unhide layers or objects while modeling
Walk through: the view of a moving observer along a path at a single eye height
Wireframe: SketchUp display of just the model edges
Workpoint: a fixed reference point for construction layout and the work
X-number: the number followed by a "X" for multiple copies
X-Ray: SketchUp display of edges with transparent surfaces

# OTHER BOOKS THAT MIGHT BE OF INTEREST

This book uses 20 interactive 3D building information models to illustrate the evolution of small house design and construction

Covers construction graphics from a napkin sketch through a simple set of construction drawings. Includes piece based construction models

A step by step approach to designing, making, and maintaining a construction website including a homepage, project pages, and animations

## COMING SOON

**ADVANCED MODELING:** Building information modeling with SketchUp
**BUILDING SIMPLE:** How-to build YOUR house
**LIVING SUSTAINABLY:** A survey of simple environmental technologies

Insitebuilders

16708 SW 132nd Lane
Archer FL 32618
**www.insitebuilders.com**

Email questions or comments to:
dennis@insitebuilders.com

If you ever have any questions, comments or suggestions
for this book or others in the series, please email us.

babs@insitebuilders.com

Also, send your work, we'd like to see what you can do

a publication of

Insitebuilders
16708 SW 132nd Lane
Archer FL 32618
(352) 870-9357

www.insitebuilders.com